ANECDOTES

Heinrich von kleist

ANECDOTES

Translated by Matthew Spencer

SUBLUNARY EDITIONS
SEATTLE, WA

ISBN 978-1-955190-07-7
LCCN 2021943800

First edition. First printing.

Manufactured in the United States of America
Printed on acid-free paper

Design and typesetting by Joshua Rothes.
This book is typeset in LD Genzsch Antiqua.

Cover image "Der Chasseur im Walde" ["The Chasseur
in the Forest"] by Caspar David Friedrich, 1814.

Sublunary Editions
Seattle, WA
sublunaryeditions.com

Contents

Introduction

On the evening of October 1st, 1810, a Monday,
the reading public of Berlin was offered a compli-
mentary issue of a new daily newspaper, the first of
its kind in the city. On four densely packed pages,
set in irregular, often miniscule type, current events
were reported, such as the founding of what would
become Humboldt University, its namesake, Wilhelm von Humboldt, the eminent linguist and public
educator, being still alive at the time. Then as now,
lurid stories of crime and human misfortune drove
sales, and the newspaper's connection with the Pres-
ident of the Berlin Police (an institution founded
the year before) furnished ample material toward
that end. Art and theater criticism, announcements
of notable books published, as well as the occasional
poem or song, elevated what was, in many respects,
a tabloid operation. The name of the paper, Berliner
Abendblätter, or Berlin Evening Pages, referred to
its publication at the close of each workday. At eight
pfennigs an issue—a value of just over €1.00 as of
this writing—it was inexpensive, available to princes
and coachmen alike, and when finished, suitable for
burning as tinder or insulating a drafty room.

The *Abendblätter* would have remained obscure,
very probably, kept in various state archives and

academic libraries, material for the occasional dissertation, if not for the short stories and anecdotes, written anonymously, inserted between the news of the day, by the paper's editor and chief contributor, Heinrich von Kleist, now regarded as one of the greatest dramatists and prose stylists of his age, though he would live to see very little of that acclaim; by the time he was writing for the *Abendblätter*, Kleist would live to see, as it happened, very little at all. A year and a month following its initial publication, he committed suicide, along with Henriette Vogel, a friend suffering from terminal uterine cancer, shooting her and then himself on the shore of the Kleiner Wannsee, a lake in the forested outskirts of Berlin. Kleist and Vogel, according to eyewitnesses, teased and chased each other around the lakeside in the minutes leading up to their deaths. He was 34, she 31. The event made international news, was covered in Paris and London, with a great deal more sympathy toward Kleist, his friends observed, than what the domestic press had afforded him. In Prussia, it was a scandal, but one that brought his fiction into print and his plays onto the stage, a fitting exit for a man who viewed human existence as amoral theater.

The *Abendblätter* held promise during Kleist's lifetime, though—good sales, initially, and good contributors. The King of Prussia, Frederick Wilhelm III, was among its subscribers. Kleist had gathered around himself a circle of young and distinguished thinkers, which included the poets Achim von Arnim, Clemens Brentano, and Friedrich de La Motte Fouqué, the linguist Wilhelm Grimm, as well as Adam Müller, a literary critic and political economist with whom Kleist had collaborated before, on the literary journal *Phöbus*. That enterprise shuttered after twelve issues; the attendant personal and financial difficulties almost resulted in a duel between the two men. But the *Abendblätter* was less collaborative, in terms of column space, than its predecessor. Kleist himself supplied the vast majority of the writing. He was aided by Rudolph Werckmeister's Readers' Institute, an early public library, which shared office space, at Jägerstraße 25, with the up-and-coming publication. The Institute offered dozens of other newspapers, in French and German, along with the latest maps, encyclopedias, and scientific periodicals. Kleist, prone to bouts of periodic inactivity, submitted himself with zeal to the discipline of daily publication. He was transforming himself, working to transform himself at least, into a new type of person: the metropolitan journalist.

But the old difficulties began anew. A heavyhanded editor, Kleist made substantial changes without consulting his fellow contributors, which resulted in a permanent break with Clemens

Brentano. There were other, more public difficulties. Throughout Kleist's adult life, conflict with France had been the dominant political concern among the various German states. Kleist himself served in the Prussian Army, seeing action as an officer cadet during the War of the First Coalition. He remained politically engaged, even after he resigned his commission and embarked on nearly a decade of wandering across Europe. A stint in prison on charges of espionage hardened his opinion against the French Empire and Napoleon, converting him into an early advocate for German nationalism. Meanwhile, Prussia's defeat at the end of the War of the Fourth Coalition had made it a client state. The French Army had only withdrawn from Berlin a few months prior to Kleist's return to the city in 1809. Direct criticism of both the French and Prussian governments was proscribed. Kleist abided by the letter of the law, if not the spirit, personal convictions notwithstanding. His writing for the *Abendblätter* was studiously evenhanded, with satire aimed at all sides, this despite his later reputation as a master propagandist. It was Adam Müller who caused suspension of publication, writing a criticism of state finance policy that personally angered the Prime Minister, Karl von Hardenberg. The paper was subjected to heavy censorship. As the cost and difficulty of publication rose, the amount of original writing, by Kleist and others, dwindled. Its subscriber base, already declining before the crisis, vanished. Müller, an ingratiating figure, was able to survive with his reputation intact. Kleist, for his part, challenged a member of Hardenberg's staff, Friedrich von Raumer, to a duel over promised compensation for the censorship. Kleist later withdrew his challenge, apologized, but was left publicly humiliated and without financial support. *The Abendblätter* lasted six months before folding.

But while Kleist began, through his plays and novellas, his posthumous ascent into the literary canon, the anecdotes remained largely underread, out of print. Much of the *Abendblätter* would have been lost if not for the Brothers Grimm, who collected issues specifically for the anecdotes, considering them small masterpieces of vernacular literature. On the centenary of the author's death, Franz Kafka would find their publication remarkable enough to write a short review, intended for the *Prager Presse* but never published in his own short lifetime. "Here is a welcome sight," he begins, "the works of a master, even when published separately for no special reason, still have a valid life of their own, and perhaps in this form strike our jaded eyes with more clarity than ever." Nevertheless, their reception by critics and scholars remained ambiguous, divided. The highlights, the "sapphires

in the mud" as translator Phillip B. Miller called
them, represented "the quintessence of Kleist as a
storyteller", perhaps with the implication that a great
deal more sifting and polishing was needed.

The current translator, like the actor Herr
Unzelmann profiled in the one of anecdotes, "hates
all obstinacy" and will not dispute the charges, only
reiterate that Kleist wrote on a daily production
schedule. But journalism perishes quickly;
the anecdotes still bring out laughs, still elicit
sympathetic groans. Their variety is also remarkable:
commentary on historical events, commentary
on pseudohistorical events, ghost stories, miracle
stories, fanciful crime reporting, fanciful science
journalism, fanciful war correspondence, among
other genres and microgenres. A more restrictive
editorial approach would have diluted their
idiosyncratic charm. And so the question of whether
a given anecdote fails or succeeds has been left,
within the bounds of a short book, for the individual
reader to decide.

And it is for readerly pleasure that these stories
have been translated. As Susan Sontag observed in
Against Interpretation: "What revolted the mature
Goethe in the young Kleist, who submitted his
works to the elder statesman 'on the knees of his
heart'—the morbid, the hysterical, the sense of the
unhealthy, the enormous indulgence in suffering out

of which Kleist's plays and tales were mined—is just what we value today. Today Kleist gives pleasure, most of Goethe is a classroom bore." An indulgence in suffering but also an indulgence in delight. Kleist, for all the tragedy in his life and work, remains, like his disciples Kafka and Walser, a comic writer. His characters tease each other; they play games; they tell jokes—all to the point of death. But the effect, rather than compounding sorrow, helps to drive it away. The fortunate escape their troubles with balletic grace. The unfortunate are dispatched quickly, as if by lightning, their destruction releasing them from additional harm. This might be near to what Kafka thought when he wrote Max Brod, making reference to the primitive balloons that were once customarily hung beside tavern doorways. "Kleist" he wrote, "inflates me like an old pig bladder."

—*Matthew Spencer*

Note on the Selection

The selection of the anecdotes largely follows that
contained in *Heinrich von Kleist: Werke und Briefe
in vier Bänden*, published by Aufbau Verlag in 1978
and accessed through zeno.org. Two longer stories,
"The Beggarwoman of Locarno" and "Saint Cecelia,
or the Power of Music" have been included because of
their first appearance in the *Abendblätter*. But since
these translations are a literary rather than historical
project, the vast majority of the material published in
the newspaper has been omitted. Readers of German
can find the *Abendblätter* reproduced in full at
kleist-digital.de. Three pieces, not typically grouped
within Kleist's literary work, have also been included
for their satirical punch: "Useful Inventions: An
Outline for a Cannonball Postal System", "A Letter
from a Berliner to the Editors of the Abendblätter",
and "On the Airship Journey of October 15th, 1810".
The anecdotes resist easy distinctions of fiction
and nonfiction, essay and narrative, reportage and
fabrication, so the translator has been granted, in
selecting material, an unusual degree of freedom.

Anecdotes

An Occurrence

Brietz, a laborer who was slain on the new promenade, said to Captain von Bürger, of the former Tauentzien Regiment, that the tree under which they stood was entirely too small for the both of them, and that he should put himself beneath another. Captain Bürger, who was a placid and humble man, really did put himself beneath another—beneath another tree, that is—whereupon Brietz was immediately struck by lightning and killed.

The Gallantry of the French

During the war, a citizen went to French General Hulin[1] and reported, on behalf of the enemy, for purposes of requisition under martial law, a quantity of logs floating in a naval yard. The general, who was then just getting dressed, said: "No, my friend. We can't take them." "Why not?" replied the citizen, "They're royal property." "Just so", the general said, giving him a cursory glance, "The King of Prussia needs lumber to hang scoundrels like you."

---

1. Pierre-Augustine Hulin was a general in the War of the Fourth Coalition under Bonaparte. He is perhaps best known for the role he played in the early stages of the French Revolution, leading a militia during the storming of the Bastille.

The Perplexed Magistrate

In H—, not long ago, a city guardsman abandoned his post without leave of his commanding officer. According to ancient law, the punishment for such a crime, once of great importance due to raiding amongst the nobility, was death. Nevertheless, the law, without it being specifically repealed, had not seen use in hundreds of years; so instead of upholding capital punishment, the guilty were sentenced, following long established custom, to a mere fine, deposited in the city treasury. But the aforementioned fellow had no desire to pay and declared, to the dismay of the magistrate, that he, because it was his due under the law, wanted to die. The magistrate, who suspected a misunderstanding, sent in a deputy for him, indicating that it would more advantageous to spend a few guilders than be shot with an arquebus[1]. But the fellow insisted that he was tired of his life and wanted to die, in such a way that the magistrate, averse to bloodshed, could do nothing, only waive the rogue his fine and declare that he, for his part, would happily remain alive under such circumstances.

---

1. A form of long gun, using a matchlock firing system, that appeared in Europe during the middle of the 15th century. The use of an arquebus, especially for an execution, would have been comically anachronistic in Kleist's day, when flintlock muskets were the standard firearm.

GOD'S OWN STYLUS

In Poland there once lived a Countess von P—, a lady of advanced years, who led a very wicked life and was, through her avarice and cruelty, a torment to others, especially her subordinates, bleeding them dry. This lady, when she died, bequeathed her fortune to a monastery for the absolution of her soul, the monastery erecting, in its own churchyard, a sumptuous tombstone of cast bronze, on which, with much ado, her generosity was commemorated. The next day lightning struck and melted away the bronze, leaving nothing but a quantity of letters that, when read together, proclaimed the following: "She is judged!" The incident (let the scribes explain it) is verified; the tombstone still exists, and there are men in this city who have seen it along with the aforementioned inscription.

AN ANECDOTE FROM
THE LAST PRUSSIAN WAR

In a certain village near Jena, where I had stopped
on a journey to Frankfurt, an innkeeper told me
that, several hours after the battle[1], when the village
had already been abandoned by the forces of Prince
Hohenlohe[2] and surrounded by the French, who still
considered it occupied, a single Prussian cavalryman
appeared; and if all the soldiers fighting that day
had been as brave as he, so I was assured, then the
French, even at triple their actual strength, would
have been soundly beaten. "This fellow," said the
innkeeper, "comes barreling in, all covered with dust,
and shouts, 'Hey there! Innkeep!' What gives? I ask
him. 'A glass of brandy!' he says, clapping his sword
into his scabbard, 'I'm parched.' God in Heaven! I
say. Don't you want to escape, friend? The French
are at the gates! 'Is that so?' he asks me, setting reins
on the horse's neck, 'I haven't had a drop all day!'
Well then, I say to myself, he must have the devil
in him—Hey, Lizabeth! I shout and tell her to fetch

---

1. The Battle of Jena-Auerstedt, 14 October 1806, in which the Prussian
Army was decisively defeated by Napoleon, effectively ending the War
of the Fourth Coalition.

2. Frederick Louis, Prince of Hohenlohe-Ingelfingen, was a Prussian
general known for his popularity and physical courage during battle,
though he, like the other commanders opposing Napoleon at Jena-
Auerstedt, was an aged man at the time.

the Danziger. There, I say, pushing the whole bottle into his hands, so he can ride away with it. 'What's this?' he asks, doffing his cap and shoving the bottle away, 'What am I supposed to do with this swill?' and 'Pour one out!' he says, mopping the sweat from his brow, 'I'm in a hurry!' He's as good as dead, I say. Here! I say, and pour him a glass; Cheers! Now drink it and go! 'Another' says the fellow, as cannonballs rain down into the village from all sides. Another? I say. A plague on him! 'Another!' he says, holding out the glass, 'And well measured!' he says, wiping his beard and leaning over to blow his nose, 'I'll be paying cash!' Oh, dear God, he should take his cash and—There! I say, and pour him a second glass, as requested, and a third, once that's downed, and ask him: are you satisfied? 'Ah!' he says, quivering with pleasure, 'Now, that's what I call brandy!' and he puts his cap back on, 'So what do I owe you?' Nothing! Nothing! In the name of Satan, get going! The French will be here any minute! 'Well then,' he says, reaching into his boot, 'God repay you.' And he pulls out a stubby little pipe and he says, after blowing out the bowl, 'Give me a light.' A light? I say. Damn you, a light? 'That's what I said!' he says, 'A light! I want to have a little smoke here with my pipe.' What? Legions are riding at his heels—Hey, Lizabeth! I say to the girl, and she holds out a piece of tinder as the fellow stuffs his bowl. 'There we are!'

he says, raising a cloud, pipe between his teeth, 'The French are in trouble now!' And with that, pressing his cap down over his eyes, grabbing at the reins, he turns his horse and draws steel. A regular devil! I say. A twice cursed damnable rogue! Why won't he get—hangman take him—back where he belongs! Three chasseurs[3]—doesn't he see them? Already at the gates! 'Well, well, well' he says, hocking a loogie and shooting them a fierce look, 'I wouldn't care if they were your ten little toes!'[4] and just then the three Frenchmen ride into the village; 'Bassa Manelka!'[5] he cries, spurring his horse and charging into them; charging into them, honest to God, and attacking, as if he had the whole Hohenlohe Corps behind him. And so, the chasseurs, uncertain of how many Germans there are left in the village, stop for a moment, contrary to their habit, and he, on my soul, in the blink of an eye, strikes all three of them from the saddle, seizes their horses—which are running loose about the town square—and then goes blowing

---

3. Soldiers, typically light cavalry, equipped and trained for rapid movement, from the French word for hunter. A chasseur is depicted on the cover of this book, taken from Caspar David Friedrich's painting *Der Chasseur im Walde* (1814), itself a piece of anti-Napoleonic propaganda. The French Empire, personified by the chasseur, is shown as isolated and overwhelmed in a Germanic forest.

4. A play on the words "Zehn" and "Zehen" German for ten and toes.

5. A corrupted version of a Hungarian oath, meaning "by my soul!"

right past me shouting 'Bassa Teremtetem!'[6] and 'How do you like that?' and 'Adies!'[7] and 'Goodbye!' and 'Hoho! Hoho! Hoho!'

"I never saw a fellow like that," said the innkeeper, "in my whole entire life."

---

6. More pseudo-Hungarian nonsense.

7. Presumably a corruption of "Adieu!" the gallantry of the cavalryman not dependent an exacting sense of French usage

MISCHIEF OF HEAVEN

General Dieringshofen, who died in Frankfurt an der Oder[1], where he commanded an infantry regiment, a man of strict and righteous character, as well as some quaint peculiarities, expressed, while in advanced age, and on his deathbed from lengthy illness, a reluctance to fall into the hands of mortuary washers. He gave his express orders that no one, without exception, should touch his body; that he should be coffined and buried exactly as he was found, complete with nightcap, nightshirt, and trousers; and asked the chaplain of his regiment, Herr P., a friend of his house, to undertake the execution of this, his final request. The chaplain promised: he pledged, so as to prevent any mischance, that he would never leave his side, from the moment the general passed until he was buried. Then, several weeks later, at first blush of dawn, a valet came to the house of the chaplain, who was still asleep, and reported that the general had already, by the midnight hour, as calmly and as gently as could be expected, died. The chaplain, true to his word, dresses immediately and sets off for the general's apartments. But what does

1. Frankfurt an der Oder also happened to be the home of the von Kleist family, where Heinrich was raised and attended unversity. A museum dedicated to the author now occupies the house in which he was born.

he find? The general's corpse, lathered for shaving, propped on a stool; the valet, knowing nothing of the arrangement, had summoned a barber who, for the sake of a decent funeral, was removing the beard. What should the chaplain do in such queer circumstances? He laid into the valet for not having summoned him earlier, dismissed the barber, who was holding the old gentleman by the nose, and because there was nothing else to be done, had the general laid in his coffin and buried, still lathered, with half a beard, as he had found him.

Useful Inventions: Outline for a Cannonball Postal System

They have recently invented, for the conveyance of discourse throughout the four corners of the world, an electrical telegraph; a telegraph which, by means of an electrophore[1] and metal wire, sends messages at the speed of thought, or better said, faster than any chronometric instrument can measure; so that if anyone, were the device generally available, wished to ask a good friend living in the Antipodes:[2] "How's it going?" the latter, in the blink of an eye, as though he were standing in the very same room, could answer: "Pretty good." But as much as we would like to crown with praise the inventor of this postal system, which in a quite literal sense rides on wings of lightning, the medium of telegraphy remains imperfect, useless to mercantile interests, good for the dispatch of very brief and laconic messages, but not the delivery of letters, parcels, reports, and supplements. Accordingly, to fill this gap, for the acceleration and multiplication of trade communication, at least within the borders

---

1. A simple device, refined and popularized in 1775 by Alessandro Volta, for the generation of static electricity, consisting of a dielectric plate (an insulating material that can be polarized), a conductive plate, and an insulating handle.

2. On the opposite side of the world, that being Australia and New Zealand in the case of Europe.

of the civilized world, we propose a projectile or cannonball postal system; an institution that would, by means of artillery stations, placed within suitable firing range of each other, lob, from howitzers or mortars, hollow shells, filled with letters and parcels instead of gunpowder, whose trajectory could easily be observed and, wherever they might fall, short of a morass, be retrieved without difficulty; so that the shells, opened at each station, the letters for each respective locality taken out, the new ones put in, could then be resealed, loaded into a new mortar, and dispatched to the next station; we reserve for now a complete prospectus, with the description and itemization of equipment and costs, pending a more extensive and detailed report. Since, in this fashion, as a little arithmetic will show, one could write, within a half a day's time, from Berlin to Stettin or Breslau[3] at low cost, and thus, when compared with our equestrian post, a tenfold savings in time is created, or even, as if by magic wand, those cities were moved ten times closer to Berlin: we believe that, for the trading and entrepreneurial public alike, an invention of prime and most decisive importance, capable of propelling commerce to the highest peak of perfection, has been brought into the light of day.

---

3. These two cities once stood at the northeastern and southeastern corners of the Kingdom of Prussia, at a considerable distance from centrally located Berlin. They are now both territories of Poland.

A Letter from a Berliner to the Editors of the *Abendblätter*

Dear Sir,

Your editorial board, in the 11th issue of the
Abendblätter, discussed, under the rubric of
"Useful Inventions," a proposal for a cannonball
postal service; a postal service which solves the
inadequacies of the electrical telegraph, namely
its inability to send all but the briefest messages,
by shooting letters and parcels at the public, from
strategically placed artillery stations, inside bombs
and grenades. Allow me to remark that this postal
system, according to a statement contained in your
very own article, presupposes the Berliner's friend
in Stettin or Breslau, responding to the question
"How's it going?" would answer: "Pretty good!" But
if he, contradicting that assumption, was to reply:
"So-so", or "Mediocre", or "To tell you the truth,
horrible", or "Last night, while I was out, my wife
betrayed me", or "I'm entangled in a lawsuit and see
no end", or "I'm bankrupt, turned out of house and
home, and set to become a vagabond", the ordinary
postal service, for such a man, runs fast enough. Since
at times such as these, ninety-nine out of a hundred
letters sent between cities are of this sort, it seems to

us that the matter of a thunder-and-lightning post, as well as a bomb-and-grenade post, can be laid aside for the time being, and we ask, in turn, if the editors could not establish another postal system which, regardless of whether it was carried by oxcart or foot messenger, could answer the question, "How's it going?" with responses such as, "Quite well!" or "Not bad at all!" or "On my life, great!" or "I rebuilt my house!" or "Bonds are trading at par!" or "I recently married off both my daughters!" or "Tomorrow, with a cannonade fanfare, we shall celebrate our national holiday!" – and more along the same line. The esteemed editors would connect with the public in a most lively way, and convinced of your zeal for the good, regardless of what avenue that might take, we hasten to apologize for taking the liberty in writing such a letter, and have the honor, with the most complete and unfeigned respect, to remain yours,

Anonymous[1]
Berlin
October 14th 1810

1. The writer of this letter is, of course, Kleist himself.

THE BEGGARWOMAN OF LOCARNO

At the foot of the Alps, near Locarno in Upper Italy, there stood an old castle belonging to a marquis, which can now be seen, when coming from the pass at St. Gotthard, lying in ash and ruin; a castle with high-ceilinged spacious rooms, in one of which, on straw thrown down for her, an old sick woman, found begging at the door, had once been sheltered out of pity by the mistress of the house. The Marquis, returning from the hunt, chanced to enter this room, where his guns were kept, and indignantly ordered the woman to rise from the corner in which she lay and get herself behind the stove. As she rose, her crutches slipped on the polished floor, wrenching her back in a grievous manner; to such an extent, that only after unspeakable effort was she able to rise again, as was ordered, and cross the room, or get behind the stove rather, where she, gasping and moaning, collapsed and expired.

Several years later, when the Marquis had come, owing to war and poor harvests, into dire financial straits, he was visited by a Florentine knight, who wished, because of its stunning scenic location, to purchase the castle from him. The Marquis, who took a keen interest in the sale, instructed his wife to lodge their guest in the empty room aforesaid, which had been richly and beautifully appointed. But how embarrassed were the couple when, in the middle of the night, the Florentine, pale and distracted, came to them, swearing high and low that the room was bespooked, for something invisible to the eye had arisen from the corner, with a rustling sound, as though it had lain on straw, and walked diagonally across the room, with audible steps, frail and slow, to behind the stove, where it collapsed, gasping and moaning.

The Marquis, terrified, though he knew not quite why, laughed with affected cheerfulness, and declared that for the comfort of his guest he would arise immediately and spend the remainder of the night with him. But the Florentine begged him a courtesy, that he be allowed to sleep in their bedchambers, on an armchair, and when morning came, he called for his carriage, took his leave, and departed.

This incident, which caused a tremendous sensation, frightened off, in a way most unpleasant to the Marquis, several other buyers; so that when rumor arose in his own household, strange and incomprehensible, that something walked about the room at midnight, he, wishing to quash the loose talk with a single decisive action, resolved to investigate the matter himself the following night. Accordingly, he set his bed, when evening fell, in the aforementioned room and, without going to sleep, awaited midnight. But how shocked he was

when, at the stroke of the witching hour, he heard
that incomprehensible noise; it was as if a person
rose from a bed of rustling straw, crossed the room
and, with a sigh and a gasp, collapsed behind
the stove. His wife, the Marquise, asked him the
following morning, when he came downstairs, how
the investigation had fared; and so when he glanced
about, timid and nervous, after bolting shut the door,
and told her that the spook was indeed a reality: so
was she frightened, more frightened than she had
ever been, and asked her husband, before he let the
matter be generally known, to subject himself to
one last coldblooded test in her company. And they
did indeed hear, the night following, together with
a loyal servant, whom they had brought along with
them, the same incomprehensible, spectral sound;
and only the urgent desire to get rid of the castle,
no matter what the cost, was able to suppress the
horror which gripped them while in the presence of
their servant, and to impute some indifferent and
accidental cause to the episode, which had yet to be
discovered. On the evening of the third day, as the
both of them, to get to the bottom of the matter,
climbed the stairs to the guest room again, hearts
pounding, it so happened that the household dog,
which had been loosed from its chain, was at the
selfsame door; and so without discussion amongst
themselves, perhaps from the involuntary wish to

have a third living member of their party, they took
the dog with them into the room. Man and wife,
two lights on the table, the Marquise fully dressed,
the Marquis with rapier and pistols, taken from a
cupboard, ready at hand, sat down together, toward
the eleventh hour, each in their own sperate bed; and
while they attempted conversation, chatting with
one another as best they could, the dog lay down,
head and paws curled together, in the middle of the
room and slept. But then, at midnight sharp, those
terrible sounds are heard again; someone, invisible
to the human eye, rises up on crutches from the
corner of the room; straw rustles underfoot; and
with the first step: tap! tap! the dog awakes, leaps to
his feet, perks up his ears, barks and growls, just as if
someone were advancing upon him, and backs away
towards the stove. At this sight, the Marquise, hair
on end, bolts from the room; and while the Marquis,
rapier in hand, calls out, "Who goes there?" and,
receiving no answer, slashes at the air in all directions
like a madman, she calls for her carriage, resolved
to leave for the city at once. But scarcely had she
flung together a few of her belongings and clattered
through the gate, when she looked back and saw the
castle encircled in flames. The Marquis, unhinged
with terror, weary of his life, had taken a candle and
set the place alight, wood paneled throughout, at
all four corners. In vain did the Marquise send in

people to rescue the unfortunate man; he had already perished miserably; and his white bones, gathered together by the countryfolk, still lie in the corner of the room from which he ordered the Beggarwoman of Locarno to rise.

An Incident at Charité Hospital[1]

A man by the name of Beyer, lately run over by a coach, had already suffered a similar fate three other times; with the result that, during an examination, conducted at Charité Hospital by privy councilor Herr K., the most ridiculous misunderstandings occurred. The privy councilor, who first of all noticed his legs, both crooked and warped and covered in blood, asked: were these the limbs injured in the accident? To which the man replied: No! a doctor had already run roughshod over his legs five years ago. Then an attending physician, who stood beside the privy councilor, noticed that the left eye was burst. But when asked if a wheel had struck him there, the man replied: No! another doctor had carted off his eye about 14 years ago. Finally, to the astonishment of all who were present, it was found that the ribs on his lefthand side, in a wretched mutilation, had been pried back on themselves. But when the privy councilor asked the man if the doctor's hackney had injured him there, he answered: No! it was another doctor who had hacked into his ribs seven years ago. And so on, until it finally became clear that

---

1. Established in 1710 on the order of Frederick I, Charité remains one of the largest university hospitals in Europe, having institutional affiliations with Humboldt University and the Free University of Berlin.

the most recent accident had driven cartilage from his left earlobe into the auditory organ. — Our correspondent questioned the man himself about this incident, and even the terminally ill, as they lay on their sickbeds, laughed at the comic and nonchalant way he related the story. — Incidentally, he's getting better, and provided he watches out for doctors when he crosses the street, he'll live for a long time yet.

On the Airship Journey of
October 15th, 1810

10:00 A.M. The oilcloth manufacturer Herr Claudius intends, in celebration of His Royal Highness the Crown Prince's birthday, to ascend at 11 o'clock in the balloon of Professor J. and, by means of a special mechanism, steer it in a particular direction, independent of the winds. This undertaking seems a bit odd, since the art of balloon navigation without machinery, through quite natural and easy means, has already been developed. For since all possible air currents (winds) lie one above another: the aeronaut need only seek out, by perpendicular movement, the current that will take him to his destination: a technique which has, in Paris by Monsieur Garnerin, already been tested with complete success.

Be that as it may, Claudius, who has quietly pondered this discovery for many years, is not undeserving of special mention. The story goes that once he found himself in the company of a scholar and asked: how much time would it take for a cloud, which had then just appeared on the horizon, to reach its zenith above the city? In response to the scholar, who answered that his knowledge did not "reach that far" Claudius supposedly laid his watch on the table, and the cloud reached, precisely at the time he indicated, its zenith above the city. He is also

said to have travelled to Werneuchen, in advance of
Professor J.'s previous flight, and gathered the people
there: for he had concluded with certainty, based
on his knowledge of atmospheric conditions, that
the balloon would take that direction, and that the
Professor would descend in the vicinity.

How today's endeavor, bolstered by this
expertise, will shake out: an hour's time should
determine. Herr Claudius will only make public his
destination, through printed leaflets, at the time of his
departure: he is even said to have dispatched letters to
this place, announcing his arrival there.—The weather
is indeed, contrary to expectations, but according to
his prognostications, exceptionally fine.

2:00 PM. Herr Claudius handed out leaflets, on
his arrival at the Schützenplatz[1], in which he promised to travel along the Potsdam Highway toward
the Luckenwalde[2] district, covering that distance at a
speed of four miles an hour. The wind, however, had
picked up enough strength by noon that he was still
busy inflating the balloon two hours later; and rumor
spread that his ascent would not begin until 4 o'clock.

---

1. A public square in the district of Barnim, Brandenburg, in the
wooded outskirts northeast of Berlin. The name literally means
"shooting grounds" hinting at the use for that space.

2. Another rural district of Brandenburg, this time to the southwest of
Berlin. By that route, Claudius would have crossed above the city, or at
least its western suburbs.

Herr Claudius was unable to realize his goal of deliberately steering a balloon by mechanical means. Whether it was because the wind, pressing on the taffeta panels, hindered inflation, or whether it was because the materials were of poor manufacture (as seems more likely): the balloon still lacked, as of 4 o'clock, sufficient power for liftoff. The public, on such occasions, always behaves itself quite childishly; and while Herr Reichard, another balloonist, taking the matter into his own hands, volunteered, without regard for the apparent danger, to make the flight, Herr Claudius was quietly led away, as a precautionary measure, by the police. Herr Reichard, that experienced and courageous aeronaut, to whose expertise the matter had been relinquished, actually climbed into the gondola; but as luck would have it, no sooner had he begun his ascent, than he became entangled in the trees of a nearby garden: but without that lucky break, he certainly would been dragged, at breakneck speed, over the roofs of the city. Later, after the balloon had been pulled down and brought again to the center of the Schützenplatz, he was asked by the authorities whether it was possible for him to make the ascent without risking his life; and when Herr Reichard answered that he could and gladly would; thought he could hardly, under present circumstances, do so without mortally endangering himself, he was ordered, in no uncertain terms, to vacate the gondola immediately; the gentlemen impresarios, once this was accomplished, placated the crowd with a costly spectacle, releasing the balloon, without a pilot, to the four winds. In less than a quarter of an hour, it had vanished from sight; whether it will ever be found again remains to be seen.

On this occasion, we must return to Monsieur Garnerin's attempt to steer a balloon at will, in a very easy and controllable manner, without any machinery. Herr Claudius seems to have been unaware of the attempt in its full scope. Monsieur Garnerin, through his interesting experiment, was able to establish two things: first, that all possible winds lie horizontally one above another; second, that these winds are subject to the least amount of change (variation) during the night. Accordingly, during August of this year, with the prediction that he would arrive at dusk in Rheims, he ascended: convinced that, with the help of a compass he carried with him, he would find, by means of perpendicular ascending and descending movements, the air current that would take him to that city. He arrived at dawn the following day, took refreshment and rested, and at nightfall, with the prediction that he would travel to Trier, ascended in the same balloon. This prediction proved incorrect only insofar as he arrived in Cologne the next morning[3]: but the experiment was decisive enough to show that there is absolutely no need for machinery to steer balloons. — Herr Claudius can find additional details in the public press.

LATEST NEWS

The balloon of Herr Claudius, according to a traveler, supposedly came to earth at Düben.[4]

---

3. The direct distance between those two cities, about 100 kilometers or 75 miles, is not insignificant, especially considering the time period.

4. A small city in Saxony, about 200 kilometers or 144 miles southwest of Berlin.

The Brandywine Drunkard and the Berlin Bells

A soldier of the former Lichnowsky regiment, a
profligate and incorrigible drunkard, promised,
after the endless clobberings he received on that
account, to improve his conduct and abstain from
brandy. And as a matter of fact, he kept his word
for three whole days; was found drunk in a gutter
on the fourth, however, and placed under arrest by
a corporal. At his hearing, the soldier was asked
why he, forgetful of his resolution, had surrendered
again to the vice of drink. "Captain!" he answered,
"It's not my fault. I was crossing the Lustgarten[1], on
an errand for a merchant, with a crate of dyewood;
just then the cathedral bells rang out, 'Bitterorange!
Bitterorange! Bitterorange!' 'Ring! devil, Ring!' I said,
and remembered my vow and drank nothing. At
Königsstraße, where I was to leave the crate, I took a
moment to rest myself in front of City Hall; just then
the tower bells rang out, 'Carawayseed! Carawayseed!
Carawayseed!' And I said to the tower: 'Ring, you!
Ring the clouds asunder!' And I remember, on my
soul, I remember my vow, thirsty though I was, and
drank nothing. But on the way back, the devil leads

---

1. The Lustgarten is a park in central Berlin, once attached to the
demolished *Berliner Stadtschloss*, or Berlin City Palace, the residence
of the Prussian royal family, the House of Hohenzollern.

me through the Spittelmarkt[2], and there I am in front
of a pub, thirty or more patrons inside, cheek to
jowl. Just then the hospital tower rings out with an,
'Anisette! Anisette! Anisette!' How much a glass? I
ask. 'Six pfennigs,' answers the landlord. Give it here,
I say—and what's become of me, I don't know."

2. In Kleist's time, the Spittelmarkt was a square in central Berlin, close
by Saint Gertrude's Hospital. Both no longer exist, though the name
Spittelmarkt has been retained for a U-Bahn station.

ANECDOTE FROM THE RECENT WAR

The most horrendous joke to ever pass human lips, perhaps since the world began, was made in the course of the recent war by a drummer; a drummer, I believe, of the erstwhile Puttkamer regiment; a man for whom, as will be heard shortly, neither Greek nor Roman history provides a counterpart. This fellow, after the Prussians were demolished at Jena, managed to scare up a rifle, with which he continued the war singlehandedly; to such an extent that, having struck down and plundered every highwaygoing Frenchman within range, he was tracked and seized by a passel of gendarmes, dragged into town, and as befitted his conduct, sentenced to death by firing squad. But once he arrived at the execution grounds, and realized that nothing more could be said in his defense, he begged the colonel commanding the detachment for one last request; and when the colonel, his officers gathering about him in tense expectation, asked the man his wish, he pulled down his trousers and requested they shoot him in the assh***, so as not to tear him a new one. Attention must be paid to the Shakespearian virtue of the drummer, who in making this joke remained true to his vocation, that of saving his own skin.[1]

---

1. Critics of the Romantic era admired Shakespeare for the conformity between his characters' speech and their station in life. As Wilhelm Grimm wrote to Clemens Brentano, "The anecdotes of

ANECDOTE (BACH)

Bach, when his wife died, had to make arrangements for the funeral. But the poor man was so used to her taking care of everything that, when an old servant came and asked him for money to buy mourning crepe, the composer, behind silent tears, head propped on his desk, replied, "Ask my wife."

Kleist are priceless, very well told and a joy to read, but isn't the one about the drummer, who preferred not to present his heart as a target, somewhat of a shot in the dark?"

FRENCH TACTICS

A French artillery captain, when assigning battery positions at the onset of battle, charged with either keeping enemy guns in check or destroying them completely, first places himself in the midst of his chosen ground, be that a churchyard, the edge of a forest, or a gently sloping hillside; then, to begin work, he draws his saber, pulls his cap down over his eyes, and while the carriages are unloaded, hostile cannonballs raining down on all sides, he, with a clenched left hand, grabs each gun crew leader (the artillery sergeants) by the collar, and indicating a patch of ground with the tip of his sword, he says: "You die here!" looking him straight in the eye. And to another: "You die here!" and to a third and a fourth and all the rest: "You here! You here! You here!" These instructions to the artillerymen, direct and unhedged, ordering them to die at their stations, is said to have the most extraordinary effect in battle, if carried out well.

RIDDLE

A young doctor and a canoness[1], whom no one
knew were carrying on an affair, found themselves
at the residence of the city commandant, amongst
numerous and respectable company. The lady, young
and beautiful, wore on her face, as was the fashion of
the time, a small black beauty mark, just above the
lip, on the right side of the mouth. A coincidence
prompted the company to leave the room for a
moment, with only the doctor and the lady in
question remaining behind. When the company
returned, it was to general astonishment that the
doctor wore the beauty mark on his face, also over
the lip, but on the left side of his mouth.

---

1. A member of a religious order of women. The title is similar but not
equivalent to that of a nun, since a canoness does not necessarily live
under monastic rule.

An Occurrence (Uhlan Hahn)[1]

The crime of Uhlan Hahn, who was executed today, consisted of this: that Constable Pape wanted him, on higher authority, arrested for some minor incident, and thus called for Hahn, down in the street, to follow him to the guardhouse, while Hahn, slamming shut the window at he which stood, answered that he would not be taken by such a ridiculous dandy. The constable then effected entry of the room, so as to remove Hahn by force, but fell, struck by a bullet from the madman, immediately dead to the ground. Moreover, when several soldiers of his regiment hurried toward the shot, Hahn seemed to want, guns in hand, to pay them his respects, and sent home another bullet into the brain of the constable, who was by then swimming in his own blood; nevertheless, he was disarmed by his gallant comrades and taken into custody. His Majesty the King has ordered, because of the unambiguous nature of the case, immediate enforcement of the decision handed down by the military courts, which awarded Hahn the wheel.[2]

---

1. Uhlan were Polish-Lithuanian horsemen, armed with sabers, lances, and pistols. Originally of Tartar descent, they served as a model for general purpose cavalry in Napoleonic era.

2. i.e. broken on the wheel, a form of torture and execution in which victims, their bones broken, were tied to a wheel and suspended in

A MESSAGE FROM OUR CORRESPONDENT

Herr Unzelmann, who has been a guest performer in Königsberg[3] for some time, is reported to satisfy the public there very much, which is, after all, the main thing; but (as can be read in the Königsberg papers) the critics, and theater management also, find he leaves something to be desired. It's said that he was forbidden to improvise. Herr Unzelmann, who hates all obstinacy, complied with this order; but when a horse, which had been brought onstage during a performance, dropped its shit all over the floorboards, to the great dismay of the audience, he wheeled about, interrupting his speech, and said to the horse: "Were you not forbidden to improvise?" At which even the management is said to have laughed.

---

the air by a tall pole, sometimes remaining, as with crucifixion, alive for hours or days, though in Kleist's time the victim was strangled beforehand. The punishment was legal in the Kingdom of Prussia until 1848.

3. Königsberg, now Kaliningrad, Russia, was a Prussian city on the Baltic Sea, famously the home of Immanuel Kant, who never left its environs. Kleist lived there in 1805, studying politics and economics under Christian Jacob Kraus, an influential figure in the Prussian civil service.

ANECDOTE (NAPOLEON)

From a work entitled, *A Sojourn with the Army in the Year 1809*. Hofbuchandlung, Rudolstadt. A Frenchman tells the following anecdote of Napoleon in 1810, a curious example of him being moved toward vivid feelings of compassion. It is known that, at the Battle of Aspern,[1] the selfsame man, deeply touched, held the stricken General Lannes for a long while in his arms. On the evening of that very battle, in the midst of grapeshot volleys, he observed an attack by his cavalry; a host of wounded men lay about him—silent, eyewitnesses of the incident report, so as not to burden the Emperor with their complaints. Then an entire French cuirassier[2] regiment, evading a superior force, overruns the unfortunate crowd; loud cries of misery erupt, mixed with exclamations of "Vive l'Empereur! Vive l'Emperuer!" the latter somewhat drowning out the

---

1. A major battle held in the outskirts of Vienna, between the French and Austrian Empires, taking place on May 21st–22nd, 1810. It was the first time Napoleon had suffered personal defeat in over a decade. Kleist and a friend witnessed the immediate aftermath of the battle and were briefly placed under arrest by the Austrians on suspicion of espionage. Kleist, perhaps hoping that his notoriety as a writer would provide a form of identification, distributed some of his poems to the suspicious soldiers.

2. Cavalry equipped with firearms and the distinctive cuirass, armor fitted over the torso, protecting the chest and back.

former. Napoleon turns about, and only by placing a hand in front of his face can he, with great force of effort, tears streaming, keep his composure.

The Ancient Festivities of Parliament, or the Battle of the Blind Against the Pig

When Maximilian I[1] held parliament in Augsburg, to move the estates toward a war with the Turks, princes and aristocrats enjoyed various knightly games. But Kunz von der Rosen[2], Maximilian's court jester and a trusted lieutenant, had devised his own amusements for the emperor. At the wine market, in the midst of a square enclosed by sturdy barricades, a stake was planted, and to it a fat sow was tethered by a long rope. Twelve blindmen, poor folk, armed with cudgels, and jammed, head to foot, into rusty armor, a spiked helm on top, now stepped through the barriers to fight; for Kunz von der Rosen had promised the swine to whomever killed it. Then, after the blindmen are arranged in a circle, the attack, with a sounding of trumpets, begins. They groped toward where, on a little straw, the sow lay and grunted. Now, receiving a blow, she began to scream, dove between their feet, knocking one or two of the blindmen over. The rest, standing beside,

---

1. Maximillian (1459 – 1519) was Holy Roman Emperor, a member of the House of Habsburg. He is remembered as a reformer, a patron of the arts and sciences, as well as the instigator of anti-Semitic pogroms during his reign.

2. Van der Rosen's name means "a sundry of roses".

heard the sow grunting and screaming, hurried over, stuck bravely, and met a fellow combatant as often as their quarry. The fellow would strike back fiercely at his supposed attacker, who had done nothing to him; and finally, a third, who knew nothing of their quarrel and thought they were hitting the sow, would strike them both. At times, the blindmen hammered so fiercely on each other's helmets they sounded like tinkers or boilermakers busy in their workshops. Meanwhile the sow, who had the advantage of sight and thus could avoid their blows, began to bellow. The blindmen prick their ears at this racket; and splitting up, cudgels in hand, they reconverge. But the pig has already sought out another place for itself; the blindmen jostle each other, they trip over the rope tethering the pig, they touch the barrier and, believing they've made contact, launch another devastating blow. Finally, after many hours of searching in vain, one of them succeeds; he hits the pig on the snout with his cudgel; it falls dead— endless cheering erupts. The victor is proclaimed and the pig awarded him by a herald; then, exhausted and bloodied, the combatants are sat down, one and all, to a magnificent feast, which closes out the festivities.

ANECDOTE (BOXERS)

Two famous English boxers, one a native of
Portsmouth, the other of Plymouth, who for many
years had heard about but never seen each other,
resolved, when they finally met in London, to hold
a public bout and decide which of them deserved
the glorious title of champion. So, with clenched
fists, in a tavern garden, amongst a crowd gathered
there, they took their stand against one another;
and when the Plymouther, in nothing flat, struck
the Portsmouther in the chest, with such force that
he spat blood, the latter, wiping his mouth, cried
out: "Splendid!" But soon thereafter, once they
had squared off again, the Portsmouther delt the
Plymouther a such a powerful right hand to the gut
that his eyes rolled back and he sank to the ground,
shouting: "Not so bad yourself!" Whereupon the
crowd, standing around them in a circle, cried out
in jubilation, and they awarded the Portsmouther,
while the Plymouther was carried away, dead
from intestinal wounds, the title of champion. The
Portsmouther too, however, was said to have died the
following day, of a severe hemorrhage.

ANECDOTE (TSAR IVAN)

When a foreign envoy, following European etiquette of the time, appeared before Ivan Vasilyevich, bynamed the Terrible, with his head covered, the tsar ordered the offending hat nailed to his skull. This act of cruelty did not faze the ambassador for Queen Elizabeth of England, Sir Jeremias Bowes. He had the audacity, hat on his head, to appear before the tsar himself. The latter asked whether he had not heard of the punishment visited on the other envoy, who had taken just such a liberty. "Yes, your majesty," replied Bowes, "but I am the ambassador of the Queen of England, who has never appeared before any prince of the world but with a covered head. I am her representative, and should I suffer the slightest insult, she will know how to avenge me." – "There is a brave man," said the tsar, turning to his courtiers, "who speaks and acts for the honor of his monarch; who among you would have done the same for me?"

From then on, the ambassador became a favorite of the tsar, a distinction which aroused the envy of the nobles. One of these eminences, who had at times adopted a familiar tone with the monarch, convinced him to put the ambassador's prowess to the test, for it was said that he was skilled equestrian. Now to prove this, he was given a wild unbroken horse to ride before the tsar, and it was hoped that Bowes would suffer no less than grave paralysis in the attempt. But the nobles suffered the vexation of betrayal through their own jealous designs. The brave Englishman not only tamed the horse, but rode it so mercilessly that it was led away exhausted and croaked a few days later. This adventure increased the ambassador's credit with the tsar, who from then on always showed him the most excellent demonstrations of his favor.

Anecdote (Capuchin)

A Capuchin monk, one very rainy day, accompanied a Swabian prisoner to the gallows. Many times, the condemned man lamented to heaven that he, in such terrible and unfriendly weather, had to walk so bitter a path. The Capuchin wished to give him Christian comfort and replied: "You scoundrel! How can you complain? You only have to go there, but I, in all this rain, must come back the same way!" Anyone who has ever felt how bleak it can be, even on a fine day, to walk back from the scaffold, will not find the monk's diatribe so unfeeling.

ANECDOTE (DIOGENES[1])

When they asked Diogenes where he wanted to be
buried after his death, he answered, "in the middle of
a field." "What now?" someone replied, "do you want
the birds and wild beasts to feed on your corpse?"
"Then lay my staff beside me," he answered, "so I can
scare them off with it." "Scare them off how?" cried
another, "When you're dead you have no senses!"
"Well then," he replied, "what does it matter, if you
lay it out to me like that, whether the birds feed on
my corpse or not?"

---

1. Diogenes, a philosopher of the Cynic school, was born in Sinope,
on the Black Sea in what is now Turkey, and lived during the 4th and
3rd centuries B.C.E. He advocated philosophy by deed rather than by
theory, disputed with Plato and his interpretation of the Socrates'
teachings, publicly humiliated Alexander the Great twice, lived in a
large earthenware barrel, and carried a lantern by daylight.

Trial by Combat in Heligoland[1]

The Heligolanders have a strange way of settling their disputes in doubtful cases; similar to other nations, where opposing parties take up arms and let blood decide, they will toss their pilot's tokens[2] (brass medallions, each with an individual number) into a hat; a referee will then pull one of them out.

---

1. A small archipelago in the North Sea, famous for its red sandstone cliffs, located between Germany and Denmark.

2. In the days before modern ship navigation, the shallow waters off Heligoland were considered especially dangerous, and local pilots earned a living by steering passing ships. In the 18th century, this pilotage system was organized into a cooperative, and members who passed a navigation test were issued brass mediations to show as proof of their qualifications.

Anecdote (Jonas)

A Mecklenburger peasant by the name of Jonas was renowned throughout the country for his physical strength.

A man from Thuringia, who happened to be in the vicinity, heard tell of that celebrated someone and decided to test him.

As he neared the house, the Thuringian could see, from his saddle, over the wall and into the yard, where a man was splitting wood, and asked if Strong Jonas lived there, but received no answer.

The Thuringian dismounted, opened the gate, led the horse within, and hitched it to a wall.

Then he declared his intention: to measure his strength against Jonas's.

Jonas picked up the Thuringian, threw him back over the wall outright, and went about his work as before.

Half an hour later, the Thuringian called out from the other side, "Jonas!"

"Well," Jonas answered, "what now?"

"Jonas," the Thuringian said, "would you kindly throw me back my horse as well?"

A Curious Affair that Transpired
During My Sojourn in Italy[1]

At the court of the Princess of St. C. in Naples, there
lived, as a courtesan or more precisely as a singer
in residence, a Roman by the name of Francesca
N., the beautiful and spirited daughter of a poor
invalid naval officer, whom the Princess of St. C.
had, from an early age, because of a service rendered
by the girl's father, taken and raised in her own
house. On a journey with the Princess to the baths
at Messina, which from there, cheered by the climate
and a feeling of restored health, they extended to
the summit of Mount Etna, the young naive girl
suffered a misfortune, having been deceived by the
Viscount of P., an old acquaintance from Paris, who
had attached himself to their travelling party, in the
most hideous and irresponsible way: with the result
that, a few months later, on their return to Naples, the
girl had no recourse but to throw her herself at the
feet of the Princess, her second mother, and tearfully
reveal the condition in which she found herself. The
Princess, though she loved the young sinner very
much, nevertheless heaped, because of the scandal
brought to her court, the most violent of reproaches;
but since the girl vowed monastic confinement and

---

1. Kleist did not, as far as we know, travel to Italy.

perpetual improvement and abstinence for her whole life going forward, and since the thought of leaving her patron and benefactress was so unbearable to her, the philanthropic disposition of the Princess, who was inclined to forgive in such cases anyway, prevailed. She raised the unfortunate girl to her feet, with the only question remaining: how to avert the shame threatening to descend upon them? In cases of this kind, as is well known, women never fail for cleverness and the necessary invention; and several days later, the Princess herself contrived the following romance to save the honor of her young friend.

A letter is delivered to her palazzo, while she is sitting at cards, in the company of a few supper guests; she breaks open the seal, reads the contents, and turns to Signorina Francesca: "Signorina," she announces, "Count Scharfeneck, the young German who saw you in Rome two years ago, extends, from Venice, where he is spending the winter, his hand in marriage—there!" she adds, returning to her card game: "read it for yourself: he is a gallant and worthy gentleman, of whose offer you need not be ashamed." Blushing, Signorina Francesca rises to her feet; she takes the letter, skims through it, and kisses the Princess's hand: "Madame," she says, "since the Count declares that he will make Italy his fatherland, I will take his hand, by your hand, and make him my lawfully wedded husband!" — And the letter is passed from hand to hand amidst general congratulations; everyone asks about the person of the fiancé, whom no-one knows, and from that moment onward Signorina Francesca is considered the bride of Count Scharfeneck. —Then, on the appointed day of the bridegroom's arrival, when, according to his wishes, the wedding should also presently take place, a coach-and-four[2] arrives: it is Count Scharfeneck! The entire company, gathered for the occasion in the Princess's chambers , rushes to the window , full of curiosity, and sees the young gentleman alighting, young and handsome as a young god. —A rumor is circulated, meanwhile, by a servant who had been sent out ahead, that the count has taken ill and must be received in private. At this unpleasant news, the Princess turns, abashed, to the bride; and after a short conversation, they both go into an adjoining room, a priest following them about an hour or so later. Meanwhile, the guests are invited to table by the majordomo, from whom the news is learned, while they sit at a most select and delicious feast, that the young Count, a true German gentlemen, is not so much ill as eccentric, disliking the crowds present at such festive occasions; then, quite late, toward eleven o'clock, the Princess, leading Signorina Francesca

---

2. A large carriage built for long distance travel, pulled by four horses.

by the hand, appears before the assembled guests, with the announcement that vows had been duly exchanged, and presents to them the Countess von Scharfeneck. Surprise and jubilation, shouts and questions: but all that can be gleaned from bride and hostess is that the Count is doing quite well; that he would, before long, present himself to everyone who had been good enough to come; that urgent business, however, compelled him to leave next morning for Venice, where, an uncle having died, he needed to settle an inheritance. At this, with repeated embraces and congratulations for the bride, the guests depart; and at the break of day, in his coach-and-four, in view of the entire staff, the Count drives off again. – Six weeks later, the Princess and Countess receive a letter, in a black sealed envelope, with news that Count Scharfeneck has drowned in the harbor at Venice. It appears that he was foolish enough to go swimming after a hard ride, that he suffered a stroke right then and there, his body remaining, for the moment, lost at sea. – The entire household gathers, on the occasion of this terrible report, to offer their condolences and sympathy; the Princess shows the unhappy letter to the Countess, who falls unconscious into her arms, wailing inconsolably, but finds strength enough, a few days later, to leave for Venice and take possession of the inheritance due to her. – Shortly thereafter, approximately nine months (that was how long the legal proceedings lasted) the Countess returns and presents the darling little Count Scharfeneck, a blessing from heaven itself. A certain German, who possessed vast genealogical knowledge of his fatherland, discovered the secret behind the intrigue and sent the young count a fine drawing of his coat-of-arms, which depicted an infant beneath the corner of a tavern bench.[3] Nevertheless, the lady remained in Naples under the name Countess von Scharfeneck, until the year 1793, when the Viscount of P. journeyed to Italy for a second time and decided, at the instigation of the Princess, to marry her. In 1802, he returned to France with his wife.

---

3. An elaborate visual pun, one which required explanation even to 19th century readers. Scharfeneck means "sharp corner" and bench, Bank in German, implies the child was conceived there, out of wedlock, rather than in the marriage bed, a Bankert or bastard.

BEST WISHES FOR THE NEW YEAR
FROM AN ARTILLERYMAN
TO HIS CAPTAIN
DURING THE SEVEN YEARS WAR

To My Honorable,
Highborn, Highly Dignified,
Stern and Steady Captain

Just as when the impetuous flood, with its foaming
waves, threatens desolation and demise on a
city entire, and trembling citizens hasten with
implements of rescue to stem the rushing roaring
tide, wherever possible, so do I hasten, willing
and diligent, incapable of doing otherwise, at the
waning of the year, to convince you and assure you,
Excellency, of my incorrigible devotion, and to wish
you, most eminently esteemed Captain, an arsenal's
worth of all that is needful for human felicity. May
you neither lack for the powder of noble health, nor
the cannonballs of everlasting pleasure, neither the
bombs of satisfaction, nor the carcass of composure,
nor the fuse of long life. May the enemies of our
peace, those marauding worries, never breach the
citadel of your heart. Indeed, may the trenches of
their effrontery halt before the redoubt of your

delight. May the glacis[1] of your welfare be held to the last by the palisades of blessing, and may the ladders of grief be thrown in vain against the battlements of your joy. May your Excellency pass, without loss or damage, through every mountainous defile on the arduous march of this life, neither lacking the cavalry of desire nor the infantry of hope, the mounted artillery of your plans outfitted with all the provender and munitions necessary for happy success. Incidentally, may I never lack for a rifle, loaded with hot rounds of gratitude, to fire salvos of your most gracious goodwill and charge with a whole platoon's worth of appreciation. I cast away the handgrips of falsehood, empty the flash pan of pretense, and thrust with the fixed bayonet of my most devoted supplication into the phalanx of your friendship, so that you might surrender the chosen ground of your affections, where I endeavor to remain, until the inevitable landmine of death is tripped, not blowing me into the air, but rather quartering my body in the fortress of the grave. Until then, I remain,

Your respectful Servant, N. N.

---

1. A bank sloping down from a fortified position, built to expose oncoming attackers to elevated fire.

The Newer (Happier) Werther[1]

In L—e, in France, there lived a young apprentice, Charles C., who secretly loved the wife of his employer, Monsieur D., a rich but superannuated merchant. Knowing her to be chaste and righteous, he made not the slightest attempt to win her requited love, all the more, since he was attached to his employer by bonds of gratitude and deep respect. The wife, who pitied his condition, which threatened injury to his health, pleaded with her husband, under one pretext or another, to get him out of the house; but day after day, the husband merely postponed the trip to which the young man was assigned, and eventually declared, once and for all, that he simply could not dispense with his cashier.

Now, it so happened that Monsieur D., in the company of his wife, went off to visit a friend in the countryside, leaving the young Charles behind to look after the running of the business. That evening, when all have gone to sleep, he, driven by what thoughts I don't know, goes for a stroll in the garden. He passes by the dear lady's bedroom, stops a moment, lays a hand on the latch, and opens the door;

---

1. The hero of Goethe's famous novel, *The Sorrows of Young Werther*, commits suicide over unrequited love, ruining the lives of all involved. Ironically, Kleist's happier version prefigures his own suicide, less than a year after this story was published.

his heart, on seeing the bed where the lady takes her
rest, beats faster, and then finally, after much struggle
with himself, he commits the folly, no one else being
around, of undressing and climbing in. That night,
after he has slept, peacefully and quietly for several
hours, husband and wife, for reasons unnecessary to
relate here, return home unannounced; and when the
old gentleman and his wife enter the bedroom, they
find the young Charles, startled awake by the noise,
scrambling, half in bed, half out, gripped by shame
and confusion at his exposure; after the shocked
couple have turned away and gone into an adjoining
room, the young man rises and gets dressed; tired of
his life, he sneaks into his own room, writes a short
letter in which he explains the incident to the lady,
and taking a pistol hanging from the wall, shoots
himself in the chest. The story of his life appears to
have ended; and yet (strangely enough) it has only
just begun. For instead of killing Charles, as the shot
was intended, it caused the old gentleman, who was
in the next room, to suffer a stroke; Monsieur D.
passed away some hours thereafter, despite all the skill
of the doctors called to his bedside. Five days later,
with Monsieur D. already buried, the young Charles
awoke, the shot having perforated his lung, though
not fatally; and who could describe—how shall I
say, his pain or his joy?—as he learns of what had
transpired, finding himself in the arms of his beloved

lady, for whose sake he would have gladly died! A year later she married him; they were both living as of 1801, when, as one acquaintance tells it, their family stood at fifteen children and counting.

A Case of Unprecedented
Murder by Arson

When the vicinity of Berlin was ravaged some time
ago by a notorious gang of arsonists, anyone with a
reverence for order, either human or divine, found
these crimes incomprehensible; but at least it was
only to steal. So what can be said then of a certain
legal case, which took place in the criminal court of
Rouen in 1808? There the death penalty, for murder
by arson, was imposed on a man who had, until the
age of 60, been considered righteous, enjoying the
respect of his fellow citizens. Johann Mauconduit,
a farmer from Hattenville, was his name. Guided
by sheer pleasure in his crimes, he would, now and
then, set fire to buildings, without anyone thinking
him the perpetrator. He possessed a device of his
own invention, which fired missiles in battery,
launching them onto the houses he wished to burn.
In the span of eight months, he committed this
crime no less than ten times, finally setting fire to
his own residence, knowing full well the landlord
was obliged to rebuild for him. But in one of his
cupboards, a missile was found, the like of which,
when they had not burned away completely, were
also found on the rooftops of surrounding houses;
and when even more proof was brought against him,
he was forced to declare himself the author of the

conflagrations which had so recently occurred in his neighborhood.

A Strange Prophecy

In the work, *Paris, Versailles et les Provinces au 18me siècle, par un ancien officier aux gardes françaises, 2 Vol. in 8. 1809*, the following narrative, of a strange prophecy fulfilled, would not bear the least consideration were it not backed by so much historical evidence. Monsieur de Apchon was a Knight of Malta in his early youth, and destined by pedigree for a career in naval service. As a pupil at college in Lyon, he was introduced to a certain Spanish Jesuit, who was considered, among his brethren, to be something of a soothsayer. This Jesuit, as he eyed the boy, said, in an odd tone of voice, that he would one day become a pillar of the Church and the third Bishop of Dijon. The Jesuit was all the more cryptic, since no such office existed in the city at the time, and thereafter de Apchon was mockingly called "The Bishop" by his classmates, an epithet he retained as a navel cadet. But ten years later, Monsieur de Apchon was made Bishop of Dijon, and later Archbishop of Auch. His contemporaries corroborate his account; and the venerable prelate himself has related the story many times throughout his life.

MOTHER LOVE

At St. Omer in the north of France a remarkable
incident occurred. There a great mad dog, which
had already wounded several people, set upon two
children playing in a doorway. As it tore into the
younger of them, who rolled, beneath the claws of
the beast, in a welter of blood, their mother appeared
from a side street, a pail of water balanced on her
head. The woman, as the dog turned away from
the children and leapt at her, set aside the pail, and
instead of fleeing, resolved to take down the animal
with her, went for the clench, arms steeled by anger
and a thirst for revenge, throttling it; but having
been mauled so grimly, she fell unconscious beside
the creature. She was still able to bury her children,
though, and after a few days, when she died of rabies,
was herself laid in the same grave.

A Contribution to the Natural History of Human Beings

In 1809, two strange and contrasting human phenomena appeared in Europe: Karoline Kopini, the so-called *Incombustible*, and Chartret, a woman from Courlon in France, known as *The Tremendous Waterguzzler*. The former swallowed boiling hot oil, washed her face and hands with nitric acid, even molten lead, and walked barefoot on a glowing iron slab, all of this without feeling any pain. The latter has been drinking, since she was eight years old, twenty jugs of lukewarm water a day; if she drinks any less, she becomes ill, feels a stich in her side, and collapses into unconsciousness. By the way, she's physically and mentally healthy, and was 52 years old two years ago.

Improbable Realities

"Three stories," said an old retired officer at a party, "are of a kind that, while I believe them implicitly, you might think me a windbag were I to tell them. People demand, as the first condition of truth, that it appear probable; and yet, as experience teaches, probability is not always on the side of truth."[1]

"Tell them anyway!" the company demanded, "Tell them anyway!" For the officer was known as a cheerful and esteemed man, who was not in the habit of lying.

The officer laughed and said he would happily grant them their request, but declared once more, beforehand, that in this particular case he was not seeking to convince anyone.

The company promised, for their part, to give him a fair hearing; they only asked that he get on with telling the stories, and listened attentively.

"On the march, during the Rhine Campaign in 1792,"[2] the officer began, "I happened to notice,

---

1. This saying appears elsewhere in Kleist's writing, notably at the conclusion of his novella *Michael Kohlhaas*.

2. The Rhineland was an important theater of action during the War of the First Coalition, fought between the French Republic and various allied states, including Austria, Prussia, and Great Britain. Kleist himself was familiar with the setting. He served as a cadet in the Prussian Army during this campaign, participating in the Siege of Mainz (1793) among other actions, though the degree to which he saw

after a skirmish with the enemy, a soldier marching along briskly, rank and file, with rifle and pack, although he had been shot through the middle of his chest: you could see the hole in the strap of his ammunition pouch, where the bullet had entered, and another behind, in his jacket, where the bullet had come out again. The officers, who could hardly believe their eyes, urged him repeatedly to fall back and let himself be bandaged; but the soldier maintained that he felt no pain at all, and begged not be separated from his regiment on account of the 'ricochet', as he called it. That evening, after we had made camp, a surgeon, who was called to examine the wound, found that the bullet, not having force enough to penetrate the breastbone, had rebounded off it, slithered between the ribcage and skin, which gave way in an elastic manner, around the entire body, finally hitting the spinal column, where it resumed its earlier perpendicular course, and burst through the skin once more. This minor fleshwound, moreover, caused nothing more than a slight fever in the patient; and after a couple of days, he was back in the ranks."

"How's that?" asked some of the company, thinking they had not heard him correctly.

"The bullet? It went in a circle? Around the entire body?"

---

combat is unknown.

They could hardly suppress their laughter.

"That was the first story," said the officer, taking a pinch of tobacco, and fell silent.

"Heavens above!" a country squire exclaimed, "Your stories really are impossible to believe!"

"Eight years later," said the officer, "a friend and I were in the village of Königstein, in Saxony, close to which, as is well known, perhaps half an hour away, on the ridge of a very steep, perhaps three-hundred-foot-tall bank of the Elbe, a considerable stone quarry is found. The workmen, when they are dealing with a huge block and cannot work on it with ordinary tools, will throw solid objects, especially ceramic pipes, into the rift, counting on the wedgelike action of their impact to pry the block from the surrounding rockface. It just so happened that during our visit a tremendous block, measuring several thousands of cubic feet, was ready to be dropped onto the riverbank; such an event is remarkable to observe, because of the weird thunderous reverberations that echo throughout the mountains, along with other unpredictable phenomena resulting from tremors underground: and so, we went out, my friend and I, like so many other inhabitants of the village, to catch a glimpse of when the block might fall. But the block fell at noon, while we were dining at the Gasthof zu Königstein; and it was not until five in the evening that we had the time to walk out and inquire as to what had happened. And what did happen? Well, you must know, first of all, that between the rockface and the riverbed there was still a considerable stretch of land, perhaps fifty feet wide, which accounts for why the block did not fall directly into the Elbe (a rather weighty detail, I must say) but landed instead on the sandy surface of the bank. A barge, gentlemen—such was the effect of the falling block and extraordinary air pressure it created—was thrown onto dry land—a barge, about 60 feet long and 30 feet wide, heavily freighted with lumber, lay on the opposite bank of the Elbe—these two eyes of mine saw it there on the sand—what can I say?—these two eyes of mine saw laborers still hard at work the following day, with levers and rollers, trying to float the barge again. It is probable that the entire Elbe (the surface of it, at least) momentarily spilled out and over the opposite bank, leaving the barge there as a solid body, just as a piece of wood will remain balanced on the flat rim of a pot, after the water it floats upon is disturbed."

"And the block," the company asked, "it didn't fall into the river?"

"No!" the officer repeated.

"How odd!"

The country squire declared that the officer really did know how to choose examples illustrating his thesis.

"The third story," continued the officer, "took

place during the Dutch Wars of Independence[3], at the siege of Antwerp by the Duke of Parma. The Duke had, by means of a floating bridge, blockaded the River Scheldt, while the Antwerpians worked, for their part, on their side, under the direction of a skilled Italian, to set fireships against the bridge, thereby blowing it to pieces. At the precise moment, gentlemen, when the vessels are floating downstream toward the bridge, an officer cadet is standing with his banner, please note, on the left bank of the Scheldt, beside the Duke of Parma—and it's precisely then, you see, precisely then that the explosion takes place—and the cadet, hide and hair, banner and pack, without the least thing happening on his trip, is presently on the right side of the bank. And there the Scheldt, as you well know, gentlemen, is only a brief cannonshot wide.

"Have you understood?"

"Ah, the devil take you!" exclaimed the country squire.

"Dixi!"[4] said the officer, who took his hat and cane and departed.

---

3. The Dutch Wars of Independence, also known as the Eighty Years War, took place between 1568 and 1648, when provinces forming the modern countries of Belgium, Luxembourg, and the Netherlands won political autonomy from the Spanish Habsburg dynasty.

4. Latin for "I have spoken", customarily said to declare that the matter is settled.

"Captain!" the others called after him, laughing, "Captain!" They wished to know the source, at least, of his last adventure story, which he supposedly believed.

"Let him go," said one of the company, "The story is found in the appendix to Schiller's *History of the Revolt of the Low Countries*, where the author expressly remarks that, while a poet could scarcely make use of such facts, the historian is obliged, in view of unimpeachable sources and conformity among witnesses, to take them into account."

SIRENS AND AQUARIANS

In the *Weiner Zeitung* of July 30th, 1803, a story is
related of fishermen on the Königsee[1] in Hungary,
who had observed several times, during their work,
a sort of naked, as they said, four-footed creature,
without being able to identify the species, for if
anyone ever showed themselves, it quickly ran from
shore into the water, disappearing. The fishermen
bided their time, until the spring of 1776, when
they finally caught, in their outspread nets, the
reputed beast. But when it was hauled up, they were
astonished to find it was a man. They brought him
immediately to the princely steward at Kapuvar. The
latter made a report to the administration, which
then issued an order for the aquarian's safekeeping,
placing him in the custody of a trabant[2] bodyguard.
At the time, he was about 17 years old, of sound and
well-ordered development, though his limbs were

1. Lake Neusiedl, or Fertő in Hungarian, as it is called today, is a large
shallow endorheic lake on the border of Austria and Hungary. Its level,
which naturally fluctuates a great deal, is now controlled by a system
of canals and sluices, which, as Kleist mentions, was begun in the early
19th century.

2. A trabant was a member of a royal or princely bodyguard,
customarily armed with a halberd. Trabants characteristically traveled
by foot rather than on horseback. They also provided the namesake,
rather ironically, for the brand of infamously poor-quality cars
manufactured in East Germany.

crooked, hands and feet, from crawling; between his toes and fingers was a delicate webbing of skin, similar to a duck's; he could swim as well as any aquatic animal, and most of his body was covered in scales.

The aquarian was taught to walk, and was initially given only fish and crabs for nourishment, which he consumed with the greatest appetite; a large vat was also filled with water, where he bathed with evident delight. Clothes were often a burden to him, and he cast them off until, bit by bit, he became used to dressing himself. But none could accustom him to pastries, vegetables, or dishes of cooked meat, which his stomach could not bear; he learned how to speak and could pronounce many words, worked diligently, and was obedient and mild. After three quarters of a year had passed, and he was no longer being watched so closely, he went onto the castle bridge, saw the moat filled with water, and jumped in with his clothes on, disappearing.

Measures were taken to recapture the aquarian, but all searching proved vain, and in the rare instances he was ever seen again, especially during the construction of a canal to the Königsee in 1803, no one was able to get their hands on him.

This incident sheds light on certain marine phenomena, previously thought legendary, called sirens. Hudson, the discoverer of Greenland, saw one during his second voyage, on June 15th, 1608, his entire crew along with him. She swam to the side of the ship, staring them straight on. From head to torso, she resembled a woman of ordinary stature. Her skin was white; she had long black hair fluttering about the shoulders. When the siren turned about, the sailors saw her fishtail, which resembled that of a common porpoise and was spotted like a mackerel's. – After a furious storm in the year 1740, which breached the dykes of West Frisia, another siren was found in a flooded meadow. She was brought to Haarlem, given clothes, and taught the craft of spinning. She ate ordinary food and lived for some years; but she never learned how to speak, her voice resembling the groans of a dying man. Always she demonstrated a strong desire for the sea. – In 1560, fishermen off the island of Ceylon caught several such monsters in their nets at once. Dimas Bosquez of Valence, who, in the presence of several missionaries, examined and anatomized some who had died, found that all internal parts were very consistent with that of human anatomy. – And here one must include the Neapolitan *Colapesce*, or Fish Nicholas[3], an

---

3. A popular legendary creature of the Mediterranean, the Colapesce was considered generally helpful to fisherman and mariners. There are numerous variations of the legend in which a boy named Nicholas is transformed into an aquatic creature. The Sicilian version has him

authentic description of which can be found in Gehler's *Physical Lexicon*.[4]

4. Johann Samuel Traugott Gehler (1751-1795) was a German lawyer, politician, physicist, and writer. His dictionary of the physical sciences, which Kleist cites, was a very successful work of popular science.

A STRANGE LEGAL CASE IN ENGLAND

It is known that in England every defendant has
twelve jurors of his own class to serve as judges, who
must be unanimous in their verdict and remain, so
the decision is not postponed for too long, behind
locked doors without food or drink, until they are
of a single mind. Two gentlemen, living a few miles
from London, had a rather lively argument in the
presence of witnesses; one threatened the other,
saying that he would, before the day was out, regret
of his behavior. Towards evening, this gentleman
was found shot to death; suspicion naturally fell the
person who had made those threats. He was taken
into custody, a trial followed, still more evidence
was produced, and eleven jurors condemned him to
death; a twelfth alone dissented, thinking the man
innocent.

His colleagues begged him to give reasons for
believing this; but he would not enter into a debate,
merely persisting in his opinion. It was already late
into the night, and hunger plagued the jurors; one
finally stood and declared that it was better for a
guilty man to go free than for twelve innocents
to starve; a pardon was therefore issued, but the
circumstances that had compelled the court were also
cited. The public was strongly against the stubborn
juror; the matter eventually came before the King,

who summoned him; the gentleman appeared, and after the King had given word that candor would not be detrimental, he explained to the monarch that, returning home in darkness after a hunt, he had accidently discharged his rifle and killed the other unfortunate gentleman, who was standing hidden behind a bush. "Since I had no witnesses," he continued, "to my deed or to my innocence, I kept silent and waited; but when I heard that an innocent man was being charged, I did everything in my power to become a member of the jury, resolved to starve myself rather than let the accused perish."

The King remained true to his word, and the gentleman received his own pardon.

The Story of a
Remarkable Single Combat

Jean Courage, knight and vassal to the Count of
Alençon[1], was obliged, for matters concerning his
estate, to journey across the sea. His young and
beautiful wife he left behind at his chateau. Another
vassal of the Count, named Jacques the Gray, fell
violently in love with the lady. Witnesses later
testified in court that, at such and such hour, on such
and such day, in such and such month, he mounted
the count's horse and visited her at Argenteuil[2], where
she was staying. The lady received him as a friend and
comrade of her husband, showing him through the
entire chateau. He also wished to see the lookout post
or watchtower, and the lady took him there alone,
without even a servant to accompany them.

As soon as they were in the tower, Jacques, who
was very strong, locked the door, took the lady in
his arms, and gave himself entirely to his passion.
"Jacques! Jacques!" said the lady, weeping, "You
have insulted me, but my disgrace will come back to
haunt you, as soon as my husband returns." Jacques
paid little heed to the threat, mounted his horse, and

---

1. A county, now commune, in Normandy, France. Courage's overseas
estates are presumably in England.

2. A town outside Paris.

rode back at full gallop. Around four o'clock in the morning he'd been present at the count's residence, and around nine that same morning he appeared for muster—facts which must be noted. Jean Courage finally returned from his journey, and his wife received him with the most vivid proofs of her affection. But that evening, when Courage had retired to their bedchamber, she paced up and down the room for a long while, crossed herself at times, then finally dropped to her knees before his bed, tearfully disclosing what had happened to her. This at first he did not want to believe, but finally he had to trust the solemn oaths and repeated protestations of his wife; and now his only thought was for revenge. He gathered his kinsmen and hers, and the opinion of all was that the matter should be brought to the Count and left for him to decide.

The Count summoned both parties, heard their testimony, and after much argumentation back and forth, concluded that the lady must have dreamt the whole affair, since it was impossible for a man to travel 23 miles and commit the act of which he was accused, with all the incidental circumstances, in such a brief period as five and a half hours, the period in which Jacques had been absent. The Count of Alençon therefore ordered no further discussion of the affair. But Courage, a knight, a man of feeling and sensitive to points of honor, was not halted by the decision and pleaded his case before the Parliament of Paris. The assembly ruled for a decision by single combat. The King, who was at Sluys in Flanders at the time, sent a courier with orders to postpone the duel until his return, for he wished to be present himself. The Dukes of Berry, Burgundy, and Bourbon also came to Paris to partake in this spectacle. The Square of St. Catherine was selected as the dueling ground, and stands erected for the spectators. The combatants appeared, armed and armored from head to toe. The lady sat in her carriage, dressed in black. Her husband approached and said, "Madame, for your honor, and on your word, I will now put my life in the balance and fight Jacques the Gray; no one knows better than you whether my cause is good and just." "Chevalier," answered the lady, "you can rely on the justice of your cause and go into battle with confidence." Courage then took her hand, kissed it, made the sign of the cross, and entered the dueling ground. The lady remained in prayer throughout. Their situation was critical: if Courage were vanquished, he would be hanged and she burnt without pity. With field and sun divided equally between the combatants, they mounted and charged, lances at full tilt. But each was too adroit for the other, so they dismounted and took to the sword. Courage was wounded in the thigh; his friends trembled for him; his wife seemed more dead than alive. But he pressed his opponent with such fury and skill that he threw him to the ground and thrust his sword into his chest. He then turned to the spectators and with a loud voice asked them if he had discharged his duty. The crowd was unanimous. "Yes!" they answered. The executioner immediately seized the corpse of Jacques the Grey and hung it from the gallows. Jean Courage threw himself at the feet of the King, who praised his valor and issued one thousand livres to him on the spot, decreed a lifelong annuity of an additional two hundred, and appointed his son to the service of the royal chamber. Courage now rushed to his wife, embraced her for all to see, and went with her to church, thanking God at the alter and offering their gratitude.

Froissart[3] tells this story, and it is fact.

---

3. Jean Froissart (c.1337-1405) was a French speaking poet and court historian. His *Chronicles* are an important source on the Hundred Years War as well as the society of medieval France and England, the two main belligerents.

A GHOSTLY APPARITION

At the beginning of autumn 1809, in the vicinity of Schlan (a small town four miles from Prague, on the road to Saxony) rumor spread of a ghostly apparition that a peasant lad from Stredokluk (a village halfway between Schlan and Prague) had encountered. This rumor became so loud and widespread that the district authorities at Schlan decided to launch an inquiry into the matter, appointing a special commission, from whose records the following story is drawn, along with oral reports given on the spot.

A peasant lad from Stredokluk, around 11 years old, named Joseph, known to his family and indeed to the entire village as a notorious dullard, slept customarily with an old uncle and some other siblings, apart from his parents, in a particular room. One night, he's jolted from sleep, and as he awakens in fright, he glimpses a figure slowly retreating from his bedside, vanishing into the darkness. Joseph, who loves sleeping most of all, greatly resents the wanton disturbance, and believing the figure was his uncle teasing him, begins to complain volubly, refusing to tolerate such jokes. The uncle, an elderly invalid, also wakes from the noise, inquiring rather harshly about its cause, and when Joseph confronts him about being teased and deprived of sleep,

the old soldier erupts in anger, uttering various
oaths and protestations, which nevertheless fail
to convince our dear Joseph, so he rises from bed,
grabs a stick, lending weight to his argument, and
thrashes his unbelieving nephew. Joseph screams
terribly, all his siblings wake and scream with him,
their parents rush over, fearing arson or murder,
but soon calm down, seeing that it's only their idiot
Joseph being beaten a little. They ask for the cause
of the commotion; Joseph tells his story, sobbing;
the uncle curses the liar, loudly; the debate grows
too pointed for the parents; now is not the time
for an investigation, and since Joseph stands by his
story, the parents join with the uncle, for the sake of
brevity, and thrash the boy together, sending him
off to bed. The charade resumes the following night,
Joseph is awakened again, sees the figure again, takes
it for his uncle again, and because this time around
he is more confident in his belief, he complains even
more vehemently; the uncle wakes up, beats him,
the parents come over, beat him too, and Joseph
takes refuge, a good deal wearier than on the night
previous, back in his bed. On the third night: the
same apparition, but not the same beating. In the
mind of idiot Joseph, there gradually develops a
conception of how the weak are eternally mistreated,
and so he remains silent and tries, with an extremely
morose face, to go back to sleep, which he succeeds

in doing. The following day Joseph comes home from the fields at evening and tells his mother how a strange gentleman had appeared to him at noontime, dressed in a white coat, with a very pale face; how the gentleman, though Joseph was terrified and wanted to run away, had courteously persuaded him not to be afraid, had said that he meant well and that he would reward Joseph if he were nice and obedient. When Joseph had calmed down, the strange gentleman said, with a heartsick expression, that he had been waiting for the lad for a very very long time, and that it was he who had appeared to him these past three nights, and that he was now coming to ask a service of the boy, swearing that Joseph would have no cause to regret it. Tomorrow, namely at sunrise, he was to go, equipped with a spade, into the fields and dig on a particular spot that the gentleman would show to him; there, he would find human bones, bound with five iron rings; these would be the gentleman's bones, over which his spirit had wandered for half a millennium, without rest, without repose; and if Joseph were to find the bones, he should dig deeper, for there he would discover five sealed earthenware chests; what he should do with them, he would discover later. Once the gentleman had said all this, he disappeared, Joseph knew not where. The mother listened openmouthed, full of wonderment at her son, who in his idiot helplessness could barely string half a dozen words together otherwise, and was now recounting his tale with the utmost fluency, in purest Bohemian. But regardless of how uncanny it was in the telling, the mother caught the scent, being a clever woman, of something like treasure hidden within the promised chests, and so resolved, for the sake of that treasure, to go along with Joseph on his adventure.

The next morning, son and mother rose at the crack of dawn, equipped themselves for digging, and ventured out to the field where the spirit had made its appearance. But no sooner had they come to the village, when Joseph said: "Look, mother! The gentleman is here already." "Where!" she cried, turning pale and crossing herself from head to toe. "Right here" Joseph answered, "he told me he was coming to lead us." The mother saw nothing; the spirit, visible only to the chosen boy, went quietly before them. The journey led across country, toward a heath with a cartway running alongside it; Joseph halts and says: "Here, mother. Here we should dig." She, with cold sweat on her brow, sets about digging with the spade; has dug about two feet deep, when she strikes upon human remains. "The gentleman looks kindly on our efforts," Joseph assures his mother, for whom the benevolence of a five-hundred-year-old spirt has little meaning, with incantations, hymns, and aves in a vivid jumble growing louder and louder in her thoughts. More bones are unearthed, covered by a layer of mold, and crumbling into ash upon contact with the air, around which, just above the joints of the hands and feet, lay strong iron bands. All of a sudden, Joseph calls down to his mother: "Mother, the gentleman wants you to dig a little more to the right there; where he points with his sword, that's where his head lies." The mother obeys, and after a few spadefuls of earth, she lifts out a skull, its brow encompassed by a large iron ring. Now she has reached the end of her tether; with every bone exhumed, her sense of fear and inner alarm grew; half in desperation, she had looked for the skull, the sight of it completing that emotion; she threw down the spade and fled, screaming loudly, back to the village. Joseph did not understand his mother, for he had never before felt so comfortable in his own skin. He tried to ask the gentleman what all of this meant, but found that he had disappeared; shaking his head, Joseph placed the five rings around the spade, played a little with the bone ash, and then went cheerfully back to the village. The five rings were later deposited at the office of the courts, where they can still be seen.

When the commission ended its investigation into the affair, without coming to any definite conclusion, a certain high official, intrigued by the five rings, authorized further excavations, ex officio, in search of the promised five chests. In November 1809, when our correspondent saw the pit himself, it had already reached a considerable depth. Since further operations exceeded the capacity of ordinary day laborers, mineworkers were brought in to avoid the charge of taking half measures. These miners enlarged the site, excavating tunnels right and left; searching for hollow sounds in the earth, they dug and dug, though not for long; the chests did not appear; rubble was encountered, hopes rose; the rubble was sifted, hopes fell. But in the perplexity of the moment, it occurred to one clever mind that treasures have their own caprices, which demand respect, and will not fall into the grasp of the heavy handed, but are only touched by sympathetic fingers, and so a proposal was made for Joseph to come and be present for the excavations going forward.

Since they had already made a great deal of progress in December, the poor boy was bundled up, given a spade in hand, and tasked with carrying shovelfuls of earth back and forth. Much was expected of this ruse, but it seemed as if the spirit was more concerned with its earthly remains than with the chests, for the even presence of our dear Joseph accomplished nothing. Increasing frost put an end to the search; it was decided that work should resume in the spring, but those plans were abandoned. Incidentally, the spirt was not as ungrateful to Joseph as would appear at first glance; for even if he did not manifest the treasure, which, by the way, was never promised, he likely did establish the custom of folk coming from far and wide to visit with the little spiritualist and shower him with gifts.

Saint Cecelia or
the Power of Music
(A Legend)

Toward the end of the sixteenth century, when
iconoclasm[1] raged in the Netherlands, three brothers,
young students at Wittenberg, and a fourth,
employed as a preacher in Antwerp, met in the city
of Aachen. They were there to claim an inheritance,
which had come down from an elderly uncle, whom
none of them knew, and having no one else they
could rely upon, took their lodgings at an inn. After
the lapse of some days, which they spent listening
to the preacher's account of the strange events that
had taken place in the Netherlands, it so happened
that the nuns at the convent of St. Cecelia, which at
the time stood just outside the city gates, were to
solemnly observe the feast of Corpus Christi; and
so the four brothers, inflamed by youth, fanaticism,
and the Dutch example, decided to give Aachen itself
the spectacle of an iconoclastic riot. The preacher,
who had already led more than one such enterprise,
gathered together, on the evening prior, a number

---

1. Bildersturm (or Beeldenstorm in Dutch) were periodic riots by
Calvinist Protestant mobs against religious iconography in Catholic
churches and other public spaces. They took place throughout
Northern Europe in the 16th century, particularly in the Netherlands.

of young students and merchant's sons devoted to
the new teaching, and they passed the night at the
inn with much food and drink and oaths against
the papacy; and when daylight had risen above the
battlements of the city, they outfitted themselves
with axes and all manner of destructive instruments
useful for instigating their wicked business. They
gleefully agreed on a signal, at which they would
begin smashing any window decorated with biblical
scenes; and certain they would have a large following
amongst the populace, they set off for the cathedral,
as its bells first rang out the hour, determined to
leave no stone upon another. The abbess, who had
already been warned by a friend, at the break of
day, regarding the imminent danger to the convent,
vainly sent messages, on multiple occasions, to the
Imperial officer[2] commanding the city, requesting
guards for their protection; the officer, who was
himself an enemy of papism, and as such, at least
on the quiet, devoted to the new doctrine, refused,
under the astute pretense that abbess was dreaming
up phantoms, that no shadow of danger threatened
her convent. Meanwhile, the hour had come for the
ceremonies to begin, and the nuns, with tears and
prayer, in pitiful anticipation of what was to come,

2. An officer of the Holy Roman Empire, which by the middle of the
sixteenth century was already divided between Catholic and Protestant
factions.

prepared for mass. They had no other protection than the cloister bailiff, a man of seventy-one, who positioned himself, along with some armed stablehands, at the entrance of the church. In the nunneries, as is well known, trained in playing every kind of instrument, the nuns perform their own music; often with a precision, sensitivity, and understanding that is missed in male orchestras. (perhaps because of the feminine gender[3] of this mysterious art). Now, it so happened, to double their distress, that Sister Antonia, who usually conducted music for the orchestra, had, a few days earlier, fallen grievously ill with typhoid fever, so that the convent, notwithstanding the four impious brothers, who could already be seen cloaked among the pillars of the church, was in a state of agitated confusion for lack of decent music to perform. The abbess, who on the evening of the day previous had ordered that an ancient mass, originating from an unknown Italian master, should be performed, as it had been several times already, by choir and orchestra, to the greatest effect, because of the special holiness and splendor of its composition, sent down, more than ever insisting on her will, for Sister Antonia, to ask how she was doing; the nun assigned this errand, however, returned with news that the sister lay in a completely

---

3. In the German noun class system, music (die Music) is feminine.

unconscious state, and that it was inconceivable for her to direct the music as scheduled. Meanwhile, some most alarming scenes had already taken place in the cathedral, where gradually more than a hundred miscreants of every age and station, equipped with axes and crowbars, had gathered; several of the stablehands, posted at the door, were crudely taunted, and the most brazen and impudent remarks were ventured against the nuns, who now and then, on their pious business, appeared singly in the nave or in the aisles: to such an extent, that the cloister bailiff went into the sacristy and implored the abbess, on his knees, to cancel the celebration and place herself under protection of the city commandant. But the abbess, unshakable, insisted that the feast day, which had been arranged for the glory of the Most High God, must be celebrated; she reminded the bailiff of his duty, to protect the mass and solemn procession, which was to be held in the cathedral, with life and limb; and she ordered, as the bells tolled out the hour, for the nuns to take an oratorio with them, never mind which one or the other, and get on with their performance.

The nuns in the organ loft were preparing to do just that; the score of a musical work, which they had often performed, was being distributed; violins, oboes, and contrabasses were being checked and tuned: when Sister Antonia suddenly, fit and well, a little pale in the face, appeared at the top of the steps; she was carrying the score to the ancient Italian mass, the performance of which the abbess had so urgently insisted, under her arm. When the astonished nuns asked where she had come from and how she had recovered so suddenly, she answered: "never mind, sisters, never mind" handed out the score she was carrying and sat down at the organ, glowing with enthusiasm, to take over the direction of that excellent piece of music. And thus it was something like a wonderful heavenly consolation that entered the hearts of the pious women; immediately, they sat down at the rostrum with their instruments; indeed, the very trepidation in which they found themselves supervened to bare their souls aloft, as if on wings, conducted through all heaven of sound; the oratorio was performed with all possible musical splendor; not a breath stirred during the entire performance, neither from pew nor aisle; especially during the *Salve regina* and even more so during the *Gloria in excelsis*, it was as if the entire church assembly had been struck dead; to such an extent that, despite the four accursed brothers and their flunkies, not even the dust on the paving stones was disturbed, and the convent survived right until the end of the Thirty Years War[4], when through an article in the Treaty of

---

4. A complex and tremendously violent conflict, fought primarily in

Westphalia, it was nevertheless secularized.

Six years later, after this event had long been forgotten, the mother of the four young men arrived from The Hauge, making legal inquiries with the magistrate in Aachen, on the sad pretext that her sons had completely vanished, as to the route they might have taken from the city. The last news heard of them in the Netherlands, the home to which they actually belonged, was, as she reported, a letter from the preacher to his friend, a schoolteacher in Antwerp, written before the specified period, namely on the eve of the feast of Corpus Christi, in which he gave, on four densely packed pages, with much cheerfulness, or rather unbridled exuberance, a preliminary report for an undertaking planned against the convent of St. Cecilia, about which the mother, however, did not want to elaborate. After many unsuccessful efforts to find the persons this distraught woman was seeking, the authorities finally remembered that, for a number of years, which roughly matched the information provided, four young people, whose homeland and ancestry were unknown, had been living in the city's lunatic asylum, recently founded by the Emperor. However, since their illness consisted of a certain

Central Europe, between 1618 and 1648, over religious divisions as well as competition between the Austrian Habsburg and French Bourbon dynasties.

religious monomania, and their behavior, as the magistrate dimly remembered having heard, was of an exceedingly morbid and melancholic kind, this accorded so poorly with the character of the brothers, which their mother knew all too well, that she could give little credence to this report, especially because it seemed to indicate that the persons in question were Catholic. Nevertheless, being curiously affected by several of the details used to describe them, she went one day, accompanied by a court messenger, to the madhouse, asking the wardens for the courtesy of a scrutinizing visit with the four miserable deranged men under their care. But who could describe the horror of the poor woman when, at first sight, as soon as she stepped through the door, she recognized her sons: they were seated, in long black gowns, around a table on which a crucifix stood, and they seemed, leaning forward with clasped hands, to be adoring it. The woman, robbed of her strength, collapsed into a chair, and regarding her question as to what they were doing, the wardens answered: they were, quite simply, glorifying the Savior, believing themselves, such was their purport, better able than others perceive that he was the one true Son of the one and only God. They added that the young men, for six years now, had led this spectral life; that they slept very little, took very little food; that not a sound passed from their lips; except that they would rise from their seats at midnight and intone, in a voice to shatter the windows, the *Gloria in excelsis*. The wardens concluded by assuring her that the four young men were, for all that, in perfect bodily health; that they even had a certain undeniable tranquility of mind, albeit a solemn and ceremonious variety; and that they would, when told they were insane, shrug their shoulders pityingly and answer, as they had done on more than one occasion: that if the good city of Aachen knew what they knew, then it too would cast aside its business and gather with them, around the crucifix, to sing the *Gloria*.

The woman, who could not to bear the terrible sight of these unfortunates, and soon thereafter, on tottering knees, allowed herself to be led back home, went on the morning of the following day, for information regarding the cause of this monstrous incident, to one Veit Gotthelf, a well-known cloth merchant in the city; for this man was mentioned in the letter written by the preacher, which revealed that he had been an eager participant, on the day of the feast of Corpus Christi, in the project to destroy the convent of St. Cecilia. Veit Gotthelf, the cloth merchant, who in the meantime had married, fathered several children, and taken over his own father's considerable business, received the stranger with great affection: and when he learned of the matter that had brought her to him, he locked the door, and having obliged her to sit, was heard as follows: "My dear woman! If you promise not to involve me, who was a close associate of your sons six years ago, in any investigation, I will confess to you frankly and unreservedly: yes, we did have the malicious intent cited in the letter! But how this act failed, though everything was planned, everything was executed with the utmost precision, with a truly godless brilliance, is incomprehensible to me; heaven itself seems to have taken the cloister of pious women under its holy protection. For you must know that your sons, as a prelude to more drastic actions, had already permitted themselves to disrupt the service with their antics: more than three hundred villains, armed with hatchets and wreaths of pitch[5], from within the walls of our then misguided city, awaited nothing but a sign from the preacher, whereupon they would raze the cathedral to the ground. But then, at the onset of the music, with one striking simultaneous movement, your sons remove their hats; little by little, as if moved by some deep, inexpressible emotion, they place their hands before their bowed heads, and the preacher, wheeling about suddenly after a momentous pause, calls out that we should do likewise. Vainly, several of his companions

---

5. A weapon used in siege and urban warfare, consisting of rope coated with pitch and coiled into the shape of a wreath, thrown onto the roofs of buildings to set them ablaze.

94

urge in whispers, nudging him carelessly with their
elbows, to give the prearranged signal for the
iconoclasm; the preacher, instead of answering, falls
to his knees, hands laid crosswise on his chest,
murmuring, along with his brothers, forehead
pressed fervently into the dust, the entire series of
prayers they had so recently had mocked. Deeply
confused by this sight, the pack of miserable fanatics
stand there, bereft of their ringleaders, irresolute and
inactive, until the end of the oratorio, which sweeps
down wondrously from the organ loft; and since, at
that very moment, on the orders of the commandant,
multiple arrests are made, and several ruffians, who
had become disorderly, are seized and led away by
the city guard, nothing remains but for the wretched
mob but remove themselves, under cover of the
dispersing congregation, from the church. That
evening, after having vainly asked several times after
your sons at the inn, I go with several friends, in a
state of terrible uneasiness, back to the cloister,
enquiring with the doorkeepers, the imperial watch
also helpfully at hand, regarding their whereabouts.
And how shall I describe my horror, dear woman, at
seeing those four men still prostrate, as they had been
before, with clasped hands, kissing the floor with
breast and brow, as though they were turned to stone,
in passionate adoration before the altar! The cloister
bailiff, who came over at that very moment, vainly

bid them, shaking their arms and pulling at their cloaks, to leave the cathedral, which had already grown quite dark, none else being present: they pay him no heed, half rising to their feet, as if in a dream, until servants come and take them under the arm and lead them out through the main portal: where at last they begin following us into the city, although with frequent sighs and heartrending glances back at the cathedral, which shines magnificently behind us in the sunset. Gently, kindly, we ask them again and again, what in the world, what terrible thing, capable of reversing their innermost being, had happened to them; they press our hands, gazing at us with affection, cast down their eyes thoughtfully, and from time to time—ah, with an expression that still breaks my heart—wipe away their tears. Coming back to their lodgings then, they fashion a cross, delicate and ingenious, from birch twigs, and set it down, pressed into a small mound of wax, between two candles, which a maid provides, on a large table in the middle of the room, and while their friends, whose number grows by the hour, stand by their side, in scattered groups, wringing their hands, speechless with misery, and watch their silent ghostly doings: they take seats around the table, as if their senses were impervious to any other phenomena, and clasping their hands, mutely prepare for worship. They desire neither the food, ordered that morning to regale their companions, brought in by the maid, nor the bedding she piles in an adjoining room as night falls, for they appear so tired; and so as not to provoke the outrage of the innkeeper, disconcerted by these theatrics, the friends must sit off to the side, at a lavishly appointed table, consuming the dishes prepared for a large party, salting the food, as it were, with their own bitter tears; then suddenly, the midnight hour strikes; your four sons, after listening a moment to the muffled sound of the bell, rise from their sets abruptly, in one simultaneous movement; and as we set down our napkins and watch from across the room, full of tense expectation as to what might follow such a prelude, they begin, in a dreadful and hideous voice, to intone the *Gloria in excelsis*. So can wolves and leopards be heard, when, in the icy depths of winter, they bellow at the firmament; the pillars of the house, I assure you, shook, and the windows, struck by the evident force of their breath, rattled, as if fistfuls of heavy sand were thrown against the panes, threatening to shatter them. At this appalling scene, we scatter, insensible, hair standing on end; we disperse, leaving behind our hats and cloaks, into the neighboring streets, which, instead of us, were soon filled with a hundred or more people frightened from sleep; the crowd presses, bursting through the front doors, up the stairway and into the dining room, seeking out the source of that dreadful and outrageous bellowing, which, as if on the lips of sinners eternally damned, arose from the profoundest depths of flaming hell to the ear of God, piteously begging for mercy. Finally, at the stroke of one, heeding neither the outrage of the innkeeper nor the shocked exclamations of the surrounding crowd, they shut their mouths; with a cloth, they wipe the sweat from their brow, which drips down, onto chin and chest, in large drops; spread their cloaks and lie down, to rest a while after such a work of agony, direct on the floorboards; the innkeeper, letting them have their way, makes over them, as soon as he sees them slumbering, the sign of the cross; and glad to be free of misery for a moment, he induces the crowd, still present and muttering amongst themselves, to leave the room, with the promise that tomorrow will bring about a salutatory change. But alas! with the first cockcrow, the unfortunates rise again and begin again, before the cross on the table, the same monkish routine, desolate and spectral, which exhaustion alone had momentarily interrupted. They accept neither admonition nor assistance from the innkeeper, whose heart melts at the pitiful sight of them; they request he courteously turn away their friends, who had otherwise gathered in their company every morning; they desire nothing from him but bread and water, a little straw, if possible, for bedding: such that the innkeeper, who otherwise profited a great deal from their merrymaking, felt compelled to report the whole incident to the authorities, requesting they have these four men, in whom the devil must be at work, removed from his house. Whereupon, on the orders of the magistrate, they were put under medical examination and being found insane, as you know, lodged within the chambers the madhouse, which the late Emperor, in his generosity, for the good of such unfortunates, had founded within the walls our city." Veit Gotthelf, the cloth merchant, said this and more, which we, considering that enough has been said to understand the inner context of the matter, are here suppressing; and he once more urged the woman not to implicate him in any way. should judicial inquiries be made into the incident.

Three days later, when the woman, shaken to the core by this report, had, on the arm of a friend, made her way to the convent, with the melancholy intention, during their walk, the weather being so fine, of viewing that terrible site, where God, as if by invisible lightning, had laid waste to her sons: they found the entrance to the cathedral, being in the process of renovation, barred and could see, with some difficulty, if they stood on tiptoe and peered through chinks in the boards, nothing but the rose window that glittered splendidly at the far end. Many hundreds of laborers, singing cheerful songs, were busy on slender, intertwining scaffolds, raising the spires a good third higher and covering the hitherto slate covered roofs and battlements with a strong bright copper that gleamed under the rays of the sun. A dark stormcloud, black with guided edges, lowered against the convent edifice; it had already spent itself over the vicinity of Aachen, and having hurled a few more powerless thunderbolts in the direction of the cathedral, it sank, dissolved into vapors, muttering discontent, to the east. It happened that, as the women contemplated this double spectacle, immersed in many thoughts, from the steps of the extensive monastic apartments, a sister of the convent, passing by, chanced to discover who stood beneath the portal; with a result that the abbess, who had heard that the lady was carrying, on her person, a letter concerning the events of Corpus Christi, immediately sent the sister down, entreating the Dutchwoman to come up. The latter, although shocked for a moment, nevertheless prepared herself, with all possible reverence, to obey the summons given her; and while the friend, at the nun's invitation, went into an adjoining room close by the entrance, the double doors were opened for the stranger, who mounted the stairway to the beautifully appointed upper chambers. There she found the abbess seated on an armchair, a noblewoman of

serene and queenly appearance, her feet supported
by a footstool resting on dragon claws; on a lectern
by her side, lay the score for a piece of music.
The abbess, after having a chair brought in for
the stranger, revealed that she had already heard,
from the mayor, of her arrival in the city; and after
inquiring, in a humane fashion, about the condition
of her unhappy sons, as well as encouraging the
woman to accept, because it could in no way be
changed, the fate which had befallen them: the
abbess disclosed her wish to see the letter, which the
preacher had written to his friend, the schoolteacher
in Antwerp. The woman, having gained enough
experience to foresee the consequences of such a step,
was for a moment thrown into a state of confusion,
but since the abbess' venerable countenance
demanded unconditional trust, and it was quite
improper to believe that she would make public use
of its contents; she took the letter, after some brief
reflection, from her bosom and delivered it, with
a fervent kiss on the hand, to the regal lady. The
woman, while the abbess read the letter, then glanced
over to the lectern, on which the score lay carelessly
opened; and since, through the report of the cloth
merchant, it had occurred to her that surely the power
of the music itself had, on that eldritch day, confused
and destroyed the minds of her poor sons: she turned
to the sister of the convent, who was standing behind

her chair, and timidly asked: "Would this be the musical work performed in the cathedral six years ago, on the morning of that strange feast of Corpus Christi?" And when the young sister answered: yes indeed, she remembered hearing that this was so, and that ever since then, it had been customary for the score, when not in use, to be kept with the reverend mother herself: the woman rose, deeply troubled, and stood, assailed by many thoughts, before the lectern; she gazed at the unknown magic signs, whereby, it seemed, a terrible spirit described its arcane sphere, and thought herself sinking into the earth, for she had found the score opened, precisely, on the *Gloria in excelsis*. It seemed to her as if the whole terror of that music, which had so violated her sons, had come rushing about her head; she felt as though she might lose her wits at the mere sight of it, and having then quickly pressed the paper to her lips, with infinite humility and submission to divine omnipotence, she sat back in her chair. Meanwhile, the abbess, who had read through the letter, said, folding it up: "God himself protected the convent on that wonderous day, against the presumption of your grievously errant sons. The means by which He did so may, since you are Protestant, be a matter of indifference; you could scarcely understand, moreover, what I might say to you on this subject. For absolutely no one knows, in the urgency of that terrible hour, when

102

the storm of iconoclasm threatened to descend upon
on us, who sat down at the organ and conducted
the music you find opened before you. Through
testimony, recorded on the morning of the following
day, in the presence of the cloister bailiff and several
other men, and filed in the archive, it is proven
that Sister Antonia, the only one of us capable of
conducting the work, was ill for entire duration of
its performance and lay sick, unconscious, utterly
paralyzed, in the corner of her monastery cell; a
convent sister, who, as a blood relative, was charged
with her bodily care, did not leave her bedside for
the entire morning, while the feast of Corpus Christi
was being celebrated in the cathedral. Indeed, Sister
Antonia herself would have inevitably confirmed
and verified that it was not she who, in such a strange
and disconcerting way, had appeared in the organ
loft, if her completely unconscious state had allowed
her to be questioned about it, and had she not died
that very evening, as a result of the delirium from
which she suffered, which had previously not seemed
life-threatening. Moreover, the Archbishop of Trier,
to whom this incident was reported, has given the
only compelling explanation, namely that it was
Saint Cecelia herself who performed that terrible and
glorious miracle, and I have now just received a papal
missive confirming this." And with that, promising
that she would make no use of it, she returned the

letter to the woman, which she had only requested to obtain further information on matters she already knew; and having enquired whether there was any hope for the restoration of her sons, and whether she could perhaps, with money or some other means of support, contribute anything toward that end, to which the woman, kissing the hem of her robe and weeping answered no: she raised a hand in a gesture of kindly farewell and dismissed her.

Here this legend ends. The woman, whose presence in Aachen was entirely useless, left behind a small endowment, held in trust by the courts, for the benefit of her poor sons, and returned to The Hague, where, a year later, deeply moved by this incident, she was again received into the bosom of the Catholic Church; her sons, for their part, died in old age, happy and peaceful, after they had once more, as was their custom, sung the *Gloria in excelsis.*

FABLES

The Bird and the Dogs

Two venerable spaniels, made sly dogs by the school of hunger, who nabbed everything that crawled on the earth, once set upon a bird. The bird, perplexed, being out of his element, hopped, dodging this way and that, his opponents almost prevailing; but soon thereafter, too hotly pressed, he beat his wings and vaulted into the air; and there stood the spaniels, eyes big as oysters, those heroes of the deep, tails jammed between their legs, gaping in astonishment.

Moral: *Float on the clouds, and the wise gasp aloud.*

Fable Without a Moral

"If only you were mine," said the man to the horse, who stood before him, bridled and saddled, but would not let him mount. "If only you were mine from the beginning, as an untutored child of Nature, straight from the woods. I would have led you with ease, like a bird, over hill and dale, wherever I pleased to go; and you and me would have been fine with that. But they educated you in the arts, arts of which I, naked as I stand before you, have no knowledge; and I would have to go to riding school with you (God forbid!) if we ever wanted to come to an understanding."

OTHER SUBLUNARY EDITIONS TITLES

The Posthumous Works of Thomas Pilaster
Éric Chevillard, tr. Chris Clarke

A Cage for Every Child
S. D. Chrostowska

Morsel May Sleep
Ellen Dillon

Homecoming
Magda Isanos, tr. Christina Tudor-Sideri

Rationalism
Douglas Luman

The Mad Fiddler*
Fernando Pessoa

Beyond*
Horacio Quiroga, tr. Elisa Taber

Letters from Mom*
Julio Cortázar

What the Mugwig Has to Say & Silvalandia*
Julio Cortázar, Julio Silva

Rabelais's Doughnuts*
Pierre Senges, tr. Jacob Siefring

The Lighted Burrow*
Max Blecher, tr. Christina Tudor-Sideri

* forthcoming